AI and t'

Defying Odds with .

B,

Gary Covel.

CW00552697

While every precaution has been taken in the preparation of this book, the publisher assumes no responsibility for errors or omissions, or for damages resulting from the use of the information contained herein.

The Art and Science of Decision-Making Based on AI Predictions

Evaluating AI Predictions and Potential Risks

Long-Term versus Short-Term Prediction Strategies: A Comparative Analysis

Harnessing the Power of Visualization Tools

There are several online platforms that provide robust visualization tools, which can be utilized for analyzing lottery data. Some examples include:

Understanding Misinterpretations and Avoiding Common Pitfalls

Ensuring Accuracy: The Role of Cross-Referencing in AI Predictions

The Art of Prediction: Extracting Lessons from Successes and Failures

Understanding AI Predictions: The Perspective of Industry Professionals

Chapter 13: Strategies for Diverse Lottery Games

Adapting AI Strategies to Diverse Game Rules

The Impact of Geographic Factors on Lottery Strategies

The Intricacies of Predicting Multi-State and National Lotteries

The Complexities of Predicting Outcomes in Online Lottery Games

AI-Powered Lottery Strategies: Insights from Evidence

A Comparative Study of Lottery Strategies: Human Intuition Versus AI Predictions

The Role of Collaborative Tactics: Exploring Lottery Pools and Syndicates

Special Events: An Examination of Raffles and Millionaire Draws

Comparing Lottery Formats: A Statistical Examination

PredictoLot

AI-LottoPredict

NeuroBet

LottoAI

PredictPro

LotteryMaster

JackpotGenius

FutureFortune

WinPredict

LuckAnalyzer

PrizePredict

DrawDeducer

LotteryLearner

FortuneForeseer

JackpotJuggler

PrizeProphet

DrawDynamo

LottoLogic

FutureFortuna

25 Websites that Offer Free Analytical Tools

<u>Conclusion</u>

Introduction

This book ventures into the fascinating realm of predicting lottery outcomes using Artificial Intelligence (AI). As one navigates through the chapters, they will encounter an intricate journey into the mathematical complexities that lie beneath random events and the powerful capabilities of AI to analyze vast datasets for pattern detection. While the prospect of predicting the unpredictable seems tantalizing, the book presents a balanced perspective, critically assessing the practical, ethical, and legal implications of employing AI in such contexts. It draws upon real-world attempts and their broader implications, intertwining technological insights with human factors. As we chart the course of this narrative, it is crucial to underline the importance of responsible innovation and the inherent limitations of AI in games of chance. Let us embark on this exploration, seeking to illuminate the boundaries between possibility and probability in the captivating intersection of AI and chance. # Background

To fully comprehend the complexities of predicting lottery outcomes using AI, it is necessary to first understand the background of this topic. Random events and games of chance have fascinated humans for centuries, and our attempts at predicting them have been equally enduring. From ancient civilizations using divination methods to modern-day statistical analysis, we have always sought ways to unlock the secrets behind seemingly random events.

Inspiration

THE INSPIRATION TO write this book emerged from an intriguing blend of intellectual curiosity and the desire to demystify the intersection of technology and chance. As a technologist, I have always been fascinated by the power of AI and its transformative impact on various aspects of our lives. However, it was the paradox of employing such a deterministic tool in the realm of unpredictable events that truly captivated me. I wanted to navigate through the complexities of this challenge, exploring the potential and limitations of AI in predicting outcomes of chance-based games such as the lottery. This book is not merely an academic exploration; it is also a reflection of my commitment to responsible innovation, emphasizing the importance of ethical and legal considerations in the use of AI. It is my hope that this book will stimulate thought, encourage dialogue, and inspire a balanced approach to technological advancement in fields where randomness reigns supreme.

How to Use This Book

THIS BOOK IS INTENDED as both a guide and a thought-provoker for readers interested in the fusion of AI and games of chance. For those with a technological background, it provides valuable insights into the mathematical complexities of random events and the capabilities of AI in pattern detection. However, you don't need to be an AI expert to get the most out of this book. Those with an interest in the ethical, legal, and practical implications of AI utilization in games of chance will find a wealth of relevant discussion here. Moreover, the book can serve as a springboard for wider debates about responsible innovation in AI and other technological fields. Through case studies and real-world examples, readers can apply the lessons here to their own circumstances, whether that's as part of their professional roles or academic interests. In essence, this book aims to engage, inform, and provoke thoughtful conversation about AI's role and limitations in predicting unpredictable phenomena.

What to Expect After Reading This Book

UPON COMPLETING THIS book, readers can expect to have a deeper understanding of the intersection of AI and chance-based games. Technologists will gain insights into the mathematical and computational challenges of predicting random events, while ethicists and legal professionals will engage with the moral and regulatory dilemmas surrounding AI use in gaming. However, the knowledge gained goes beyond these specifics. It extends to a broader appreciation of AI's capabilities and limitations, critical for anyone operating in today's rapidly digitizing world. Most importantly, the book aims to foster a sense of informed skepticism and the realization that while AI is a powerful tool, it isn't an infallible solution for every problem. Readers will be equipped to engage in informed discussions about AI's applications in society, recognizing both its potential and its constraints, and to advocate for responsible, ethically sound innovation in AI and other fields of technology.

As we venture into the next chapter, we dive further into the world of lottery prediction algorithms and the intriguing role of AI. Prepare to embark on an exciting journey where mathematics, chance, and computing collide. We challenge you, brave reader, to step into the realm of the unpredictable, armed with the knowledge you've gained thus far. Embrace the complexity, question the unknown, and delight in the intellectual adventure that awaits! Are you ready to uncover the secrets of the unpredictable? Let's begin!

Chapter 1: Introduction to the Enigma of Lotteries

L otteries, for centuries, have been a tantalizing game of chance, captivating millions with the promise of life-altering riches with the roll of a few numbered balls. The essence of lotteries lies in their unpredictability, a characteristic that also makes them a mathematical enigma worth exploring. In this chapter, we will delve deep into the history, mechanics, and underlying mathematics of lotteries, setting the foundation for our later explorations of predictive algorithms and artificial intelligence. Before we venture into the intersection of AI and lotteries, it is crucial to understand the enigmatic nature of the lottery itself. So, let's embark on this journey to decipher the intrinsic randomness and complexity of this tantalizing game of chance.

The Ancient Roots of Lotteries

THE CONCEPT OF LOTTERIES has been woven into the fabric of human history, dating back to ancient times. In the Roman Empire, lotteries were part of lavish feasts known as "banquets of chance," where guests were given tickets for prizes. These gatherings were often organized by emperors as a way to distribute property and slaves. Moving towards the east, we find references to lotteries in the Chinese Han Dynasty, where they were used to finance major state projects such as the Great Wall of China. The lottery tickets from this era were likely a form of Keno slips, a game that is strikingly similar to modern lotteries. As we traverse the timeline, we come across the 15th century, when public lotteries started making their way into Europe. The money raised from these public lotteries was utilized for town fortifications, assisting the poor, and other public welfare initiatives. This historical journey underscored that the allure of randomness and chance, which are core elements of lotteries, have held a consistent fascination for humans across different epochs and cultures.

Unraveling the Science of Randomness and Probability

RANDOMNESS AND PROBABILITY are two intrinsic principles of lotteries. The term "random" in a scientific context refers to events that are unpredictable. No matter how much data we gather or how many calculations we perform, the outcome of a truly random event cannot be determined. It's this inherent unpredictability that gives lotteries their thrilling appeal. Probability, on the other hand, provides a measure of the likelihood that a particular event will occur. In a standard lottery, where each number has an equal chance to be chosen, the probability concept governs the odds of any given number, or sequence of numbers, being selected. However, despite the mathematical precision of probability, we must bear in mind that a higher probability doesn't guarantee an outcome. Our understanding of both randomness and probability thus forms the backbone of any exploration into the possibilities, and limitations, of using AI for predicting lottery outcomes.

The Role of Artificial Intelligence in Predicting Lottery Outcomes

ARTIFICIAL INTELLIGENCE (AI) has seen remarkable advancements, offering potential solutions to complex problems across various domains, including predicting lottery outcomes. AI, through its machine learning (ML) subset, can analyze vast datasets, identifying subtle patterns that would be impossible for humans to discern. However, lotteries, being predicated on randomness and probability, present a unique challenge. While ML algorithms can analyze past lottery results and detect patterns, these patterns are statistical and do not influence future outcomes due to the inherent randomness of lotteries. Furthermore, the ethical and legal implications of using AI in this context are significant and cannot be overlooked. Despite the allure of using AI to predict lottery outcomes, the practical limitations combined with the moral and legal constraints underscore the need for responsible innovation in AI applications.

The Impact of Big Wins on Public Perception

SPECTACULAR LOTTERY wins, often publicized widely, contribute to persistent public fantasies about hitting the jackpot. These stories of sudden wealth reinforce the idea that anyone, regardless of their circumstances, can become a millionaire overnight, fueling lottery ticket sales. However, it's important to remember that such wins are anomalies and not the norm. Furthermore, these stories inadvertently encourage the belief that AI can help predict lottery outcomes, contributing to misconceptions about the capabilities and limitations of AI in the context of games of chance. While it's true that AI can process and analyze vast amounts of data far more efficiently than humans, its use in predicting inherently random events, such as lottery draws, remains questionable. Therefore, it is critical to maintain a factual, balanced view of AI and its potential uses, to avoid contributing to unrealistic expectations and potential misapplications of the technology.

Economic Implications of Lotteries

LOTTERIES PLAY A SUBSTANTIAL role in the economy, particularly in countries where they are government-operated or where their revenues contribute significantly to public funds. These funds often support vital social programs, infrastructure development, and educational initiatives. Therefore, the financial impact of lotteries extends far beyond the individual winners and losers—it influences communities and society at large. However, it's worth noting that the economic benefits of lotteries must be weighed against the potential social costs, such as problem gambling and its associated issues. Moreover, the discussion about the economic implications of AI predictions in lottery outcomes is still in its infancy. Although AI could theoretically be used to boost ticket sales by feeding into lottery fantasies, such a use could also exacerbate the aforementioned social issues, and the ethical and legal considerations remain significant. Hence, we must approach the intersection of AI and lotteries with caution, ensuring that any potential economic gains do not overshadow the potential risks and harms.

The Mechanics of Lottery Draws and AI Predictive Modelling

WHEN THINKING ABOUT the role of AI in predicting lottery outcomes, it's vital to understand the mechanics of how these draws work. Lottery draws are designed to be random events, often employing physical processes like ball machines or random number generators to ensure fairness and unpredictability. This randomness presents a substantial challenge for predictive modelling, as the very concept of a pattern or trend is fundamentally inconsistent with the nature of a random event. Even artificial intelligence, sophisticated as it is, may struggle with this task, as its learning algorithms are fundamentally designed to identify patterns and make predictions based on those patterns. Therefore, the task of predicting a truly random event is, by definition, a tall order for AI, notwithstanding its remarkable processing and analytical capabilities. While AI has demonstrated success in many fields, its application in predicting lottery outcomes remains a highly speculative concept. This underscores the importance of understanding the limitations of AI and the nature of random events, to maintain realistic expectations and use technology responsibly.

Despite the inherent challenges, there have been several attempts to leverage AI's power to predict lottery outcomes, with varying degrees of success. Some of these efforts have utilized complex neural networks and deep learning techniques to analyze historical lottery data. However, these models often fall short in reliably predicting future draws. The reason lies in the nature of the data itself. Unlike other fields where AI has shown remarkable results, such as stock market predictions or disease diagnosis, the lottery does not produce trends or patterns that these algorithms can learn from.

That being said, AI has found its place in lotteries in other ways. It has been effectively used to detect fraudulent activities and ensure the fairness of lottery draws. AI algorithms can spot irregular betting patterns and flag suspicious activities, thus contributing to the integrity of the game.

Nevertheless, the quest for a foolproof AI-based lottery prediction system continues. While these efforts push the boundaries of AI, it's crucial to remain aware of the ethical and legal implications, and remember that in games of chance, the unpredictability is part of the appeal.

The Mathematical Complexity of Lottery Prediction

THE ULTIMATE CHALLENGE in predicting lottery outcomes lies in the mathematical nature of the game. By definition, lotteries are games of chance where outcomes are determined by random draw. In a typical lottery draw, the combination of numbers drawn does not depend on any previous draws, making each draw an independent event. This characteristic, referred to as the memoryless property, significantly complicates the prediction process. Traditional algorithms and even advanced AI models struggle to find patterns or trends in this type of data, as the sequence of lottery draws does not exhibit any predictable behavior. Consequently, the task of predicting future outcomes in a lottery draw remains a complex mathematical problem. Despite these challenges, the exploration into this area of study has unveiled fascinating insights into both the randomness of lotteries and the capabilities of AI technology.

AI's Approach to the Randomness of Lotteries

AI TECHNOLOGY TACKLES the randomness of lottery draws differently. Instead of attempting to identify a non-existent pattern in the sequence of past draws, machine learning algorithms can analyze vast amounts of data from multiple variables to possibly predict an outcome. These variables may include data from the frequency of individual number occurrences, time patterns like the day of the week or time of the year, or even correlating lottery results with other seemingly unrelated external factors such as weather conditions or economic indicators.

This multi-dimensional approach can generate a probabilistic prediction, showing the likelihood of individual numbers appearing in future draws. However, it is essential to underscore that even with a slight edge in predicting individual numbers, correctly predicting the exact combination of a lottery draw remains a Herculean task. AI technology, no matter how advanced, cannot guarantee a winning lottery ticket.

The exploration into AI's role in predicting lottery outcomes does not only shed light on the limitations of AI but also reiterates the nature of lotteries as games of chance. The unpredictability and randomness are inherent characteristics that make lotteries exciting and should remain respected.

The Human Factor in Lottery Selection

DESPITE THE ALLURE of using AI for lottery selection, it is worth noting that many players still rely on a human touch in choosing their numbers. Often, selections are based on a personal blend of superstition, intuition, and emotional connection. Some players favor numbers linked to significant life events, such as birthdays, anniversaries, or memorable occurrences. Others may opt for 'lucky' numbers or sequences they believe have a higher chance of being drawn.

In contrast to AI's scientific approach, these personal strategies illustrate the emotional and psychological aspects of lottery play. The thrill of choosing one's own numbers, the anticipation of the draw, and the dream of a potential win all contribute to the lottery's enduring appeal. While AI analysis might provide a probabilistic prediction of lottery outcomes, the human element adds a dimension of excitement and personal engagement that technology cannot replicate.

This balance between scientific prediction and human passion continues to define the lottery experience, reminding us of the limitations of AI in fully replicating or predicting human behavior. The unpredictability of the lottery, like many aspects of life, remains part of its charm and a testament to the nature of chance.

Legal Implications of AI in Lottery Predictions

WHEN EXPLORING THE intersection of AI and lottery games, it's crucial to consider the legal implications as well. In many jurisdictions, using AI to predict lottery outcomes could be viewed as an unfair advantage and potentially illegal. Laws often prohibit the use of 'inside information' or advanced technologies to skew gambling outcomes in favor of the player. Therefore, even if an AI system could accurately predict lottery numbers, using such predictions could result in legal sanctions.

Moreover, the transparency and integrity of lottery games rely on the principle of chance. If AI were to predict outcomes reliably, it would fundamentally alter the nature of the lottery, which could lead to legal and regulatory challenges. Hence, while the technological feasibility of using AI for lottery predictions is an intriguing concept, its real-world application may be fraught with legal hurdles and ethical dilemmas.

The Impact of Digitalization on Lottery Games

IN THE DIGITAL ERA, technology has significantly altered the landscape of lottery games, revolutionizing how they are played and experienced. Online lottery platforms have emerged, offering participants the convenience of buying tickets and checking results from the comfort of their homes. These platforms use sophisticated algorithms to ensure the randomness of draws and provide a secure environment for transactions, thereby maintaining the integrity and fairness of the game.

Furthermore, mobile applications have made it even easier for players to participate in lottery games. These apps often come with features such as automatic ticket checking, alerts for winning numbers, and even personalized number generation based on user preferences.

However, with this digital transformation comes new challenges. Cybersecurity is a prime concern, with online platforms needing to safeguard against potential threats. Additionally, the shift towards digital lotteries also raises questions about accessibility, particularly for older players who may not be as tech-savvy. Despite these challenges, it's clear that technology - with all its advantages and potential pitfalls - is reshaping the lottery industry.

AI and Lottery: A Deep Dive into the Probability Abyss

AS WE NAVIGATE THROUGH the digital transformation of lottery games, one question looms large: Can artificial intelligence effectively predict lottery outcomes? The next chapter delves into this fascinating query, exploring the mathematical complexities of random events and the predictive capabilities of AI. We will critically examine the feasibility of using machine learning algorithms in this context, assessing their strengths and potential limitations. Get ready to dive deep into the probability abyss as we unravel the intricate intricacies of AI in games of chance.

Chapter 2: Artificial Intelligence Demystified

A rtificial Intelligence (AI): a term that brings with it a flurry of connotations, from groundbreaking technological advancements to dystopian sci-fi narratives. But what does AI truly entail? How does it work, and why is it significant? In this chapter, we will strip away the myths and misconceptions surrounding AI, providing a clear, concise, and comprehensive understanding of this transformative technology. We'll delve into its core components, its functioning, its capabilities, and its limitations. As we embark on this enlightening journey, we will also discuss its application to our central theme: the lottery industry. So, brace yourself for a captivating exploration into the intriguing world of artificial intelligence.

Unveiling the Essence of Artificial Intelligence

ARTIFICIAL INTELLIGENCE (AI) has evolved from a concept in the abstract to a critical tool for myriad applications. At its essence, AI is a branch of computer science that strives to mimic or replicate human intelligence in machines. The term is often linked to machines or computers that mimic cognitive functions that we associate with the human mind, such as learning and problem-solving. However, AI is not a single, monolithic entity; it encompasses a diverse array of technologies and methods, including Machine Learning (ML), Neural Networks, and Deep Learning. These components, working synergistically, enable AI to analyze patterns, learn from experience, make decisions, and even predict future outcomes based on vast datasets. But AI is not without limitations. Despite its advanced capabilities, AI's effectiveness is inherently constrained by the quality and quantity of the input data it receives. Moreover, while AI can mimic human intelligence, it lacks the ability to comprehend or understand the information it processes, creating a fundamental divergence between artificial and human intelligence. In the context of the lottery industry, AI's capacity to predict outcomes remains a subject of ongoing debate and research, a topic we'll continue to explore in this fascinating journey through the realm of random possibilities.

The Evolution of Artificial Intelligence: A Historical Perspective

ARTIFICIAL INTELLIGENCE (AI) has undergone a remarkable evolution since its inception. The birth of AI can be traced back to the mid-20th century when Alan Turing, a British mathematician, posed the question, "Can machines think?" This query laid the groundwork for the development of the Turing Test and propelled forward the study of AI. The 1950s ushered in the advent of symbolic AI with its focus on replicating human intelligence through rules and logic. The 1980s and 1990s saw the emergence of Machine Learning, where computers were programmed to learn from data. The dawn of the 21st century brought with it advanced AI technologies such as Deep Learning and Neural Networks, which have transformed the AI landscape by facilitating the analysis of vast datasets and complex computations. Today, AI is ubiquitous, permeating every sector from healthcare to finance to entertainment. It has become an integral tool in solving complex problems, making predictions, and automating tasks, despite the limitations inherent in the technology. As we journey further into the 21st century, the evolution and potential of AI continue to captivate and challenge us, a testament to the power and mystery of this groundbreaking field.

The Cornerstones of AI: Machine Learning and Deep Learning

MACHINE LEARNING (ML) and Deep Learning (DL) are two fundamental technologies that power Artificial Intelligence. At their core, both ML and DL involve teaching machines how to learn by providing them with input data and enabling them to make accurate predictions or decisions without being explicitly programmed to perform these tasks.

Machine Learning, as the more traditional form of AI, uses algorithms to parse data, learn from it, and make predictions or decisions. The primary goal here is to allow computers to learn automatically without human intervention. Machine Learning techniques include linear and logistic regression, decision trees, support vector machines, and k-nearest neighbors among others.

Deep Learning, a subset of Machine Learning, takes the concept a step further by attempting to mimic the functioning of the human brain to process data and create patterns for decision making. It uses artificial neural networks to model and understand complex patterns. The "deep" in Deep Learning represents the idea of successive layers of representations. How these layers are created is a function of the weights and computation in the network, which are learned during training.

While these technologies have their strengths and limitations, they're crucial to powering AI. As AI continues to evolve, so too will these technologies, opening up new possibilities for AI applications and reshaping our understanding of machine intelligence.

Predictive Analysis in Lottery Outcomes: An AI Perspective

PREDICTIVE ANALYSIS in lottery outcomes is a challenging yet intriguing area of AI application. It requires the AI system to navigate the realm of randomness and extract viable patterns from what can be understood as pure chance. Traditional Machine Learning techniques, such as regression models and decision trees, might prove inadequate given the sheer uncertainty and lack of apparent patterns in lottery outcomes.

However, Deep Learning, with its sophisticated neural network models, may offer a glimmer of hope. By employing deep neural networks, which mimic the human brain's ability to detect patterns and learn from experience, it might be possible to discern subtle patterns, if any, in the lottery data. But it's important to remember that the random nature of lottery draws presents an upper limit on the accuracy of any predictive method.

While the technical feasibility of this approach is an engaging area of exploration, it also raises pertinent ethical and legal questions. If AI can predict lottery outcomes, what are the implications for fairness and the foundational principles of chance-based games? How would such capabilities be regulated? These questions underscore the need for responsible innovation in AI, highlighting that technological advancement must always go hand-in-hand with ethical considerations and social responsibility.

The Real-World Attempts at Predicting Lottery Outcomes

SEVERAL ATTEMPTS HAVE been made to leverage AI in predicting lottery outcomes. While these endeavors vary in their success, they all share a common theme: the exploration of the boundaries of AI's capabilities. Some innovative initiatives have used large data sets of historical lottery results, training AI models to identify potential patterns in these data. Although these methods rarely achieve complete prediction accuracy given the random nature of lottery draws, they serve as a testament to AI's versatility and potential.

Limitations and Responsible Innovation

HOWEVER, IT'S CRUCIAL to acknowledge the inherent limitations of AI in this context. Despite the most advanced predictive models, the nature of games of chance and their inherent unpredictability cannot be completely overridden. Therefore, one should approach any claims of AI-powered lottery prediction with a healthy dose of skepticism. Furthermore, the potential for misuse of such technology underscores the importance of regulation. Lottery organizations worldwide need to stay vigilant and adopt protective measures, ensuring the fairness and integrity of these games is not compromised by technological advancements. Responsible innovation should be the cornerstone of any technological endeavor, including the application of AI in predicting lottery outcomes. This approach necessitates an ethical framework that balances the pursuit of technological advancement with the preservation of fairness, transparency, and societal values.

The use of AI in predicting lottery outcomes is a fascinating and complex challenge that requires a delicate balance between technological capabilities and ethical considerations. While some may see it as a game-changing opportunity, it's crucial to approach this topic with caution and responsible innovation. As we continue to push the boundaries of what AI can achieve, we must also remain mindful of its limitations and potential impact on society. Only through responsible development and regulation can we ensure that AI remains a tool for progress rather than a threat to fairness and integrity. So let us continue to explore the possibilities while keeping an eye on our values and responsibilities towards the technology we create.

Real-world Applications of AI: A Closer Look

ARTIFICIAL INTELLIGENCE (AI) has permeated every corner of our modern world, transforming industries and daily life with its unparalleled abilities in data processing and pattern recognition. In healthcare, AI systems, such as IBM's Watson, are being used to predict patient outcomes, assist in diagnosis, and personalize treatment plans. In finance, AI algorithms sift through complex market data to generate insights, forecast trends, and automate trading.

In transportation, AI-powered autonomous vehicles are expected to revolutionize mobility, reducing accidents and improving traffic efficiency. Even in entertainment, AI has found a place, with recommendation algorithms in platforms like Netflix and Spotify tailoring content to individual user preferences.

However, as AI continues to progress and expand its influence, it's crucial to remember its limitations and the ethical considerations involved. AI systems are only as good as the data they are trained on, and biases in this data can lead to skewed outcomes. Furthermore, the use of AI in sensitive areas like healthcare and finance requires stringent regulation to protect individual privacy and prevent misuse. As we continue to leverage AI's immense potential, we must remain committed to responsible innovation and be diligent in mitigating its risks.

Understanding the Intricacies of Machine Learning and Deep Learning

MACHINE LEARNING (ML) and Deep Learning (DL), both subsets of AI, have dramatically reshaped our approach to data analysis and predictive modeling. ML involves teaching an algorithm to learn from data inputs, adapt to new inputs, and make decisions or forecasts. It is generally categorized into two types: supervised learning, where the model learns from labeled data, and unsupervised learning, where the model identifies patterns in unlabeled data.

DL, on the other hand, is a more advanced technique that utilizes artificial neural networks with multiple layers (hence the term "deep") to simulate human decision-making processes. It excels at managing vast amounts of unstructured data and has been instrumental in advancements such as image and speech recognition.

In the context of predicting lottery outcomes, both ML and DL present intriguing possibilities and challenges. They can analyze vast historical lottery data for pattern detection, but the inherent randomness of lottery draws imposes significant limitations on the predictive capabilities of these technologies. Moreover, there's a host of ethical and legal considerations surrounding their use in this arena, emphasizing the need for balanced innovation and responsible use.

The Nexus of Natural Language Processing and Artificial Intelligence

NATURAL LANGUAGE PROCESSING (NLP), another subset of AI, is a technology that focuses on the interaction between computers and humans through language. It enables machines to understand, interpret, and generate human language in a way that is both meaningful and useful. NLP employs algorithms to identify and extract the natural language rules, thus allowing systems to understand and respond to inputs in human language. It's the driving force behind voice-operated intelligent systems such as Siri, Alexa, and Google Assistant.

In the context of predicting lottery outcomes, NLP might seem a bit far-fetched. However, it can be used to facilitate communication between the user and the AI system, allowing the user to ask questions about lottery data or predictions in their natural language. This user-friendly interface can make AI predictions more accessible and understandable to the general public. However, the same ethical and legal considerations apply, and the development and use of such technology should be done responsibly.

Utilizing Artificial Intelligence for predicting lottery outcomes brings a new dynamic to the realm of games of chance. AI, with its remarkable data processing and pattern recognition capabilities, can potentially uncover subtle patterns in vast historical lottery data that might seem random at first glance. This novel approach could provide a deeper understanding of lottery draws, transcending the conventional approach of viewing such draws as purely random events.

Implementing Natural Language Processing (NLP) in this context, could revolutionize the way users interact with lottery prediction systems. With NLP, users could ask complex questions about lottery data or predictions using their natural language, making AI predictions not just a technical tool for data analysts, but a user-friendly application accessible to the general public. Ensuring the responsible use of such technology could lead to a new era in which AI is not merely a behind-the-scenes player, but an interactive, integral part of our daily lives.

The Positive Implications of Robotics and Automation in Lottery Predictions

THE ADVENT OF ROBOTICS and automation has revolutionized numerous industries, and their application in lottery prediction systems shows promising potential. Automation allows for the efficient handling of complex and voluminous data, while robotics can provide a user-friendly interface that brings a novel tangible aspect to AI lottery systems. These technological advancements can enhance the accuracy of pattern recognition, analyzing large datasets of lottery numbers faster and more efficiently than a human ever could.

This high-speed data analysis equips users with potentially useful insights, significantly reducing the time and effort required for human analysis. Furthermore, it opens up possibilities for real-time predictions, allowing for reactive and dynamic betting strategies. Robotics, particularly when allied with Natural Language Processing, could also enhance user interaction, enabling users to engage with the system in a more intuitive and accessible way.

However, it's important to emphasize that while these advancements can improve the lottery experience and potentially increase the odds of winning, they don't guarantee success. The lottery, after all, remains a game of chance. The exciting prospect here is not about guaranteeing a win, but about harnessing the power of AI, robotics, and automation to elevate the user experience, bring a new level of engagement, and perhaps, offer a fresh perspective on a classic game.

Analyzing and Winning the Lottery: The AI Advantage

AI'S CAPABILITIES IN pattern recognition, predictive analysis, and real-time processing can indeed enhance the way we approach lottery games. Traditional approaches to predict lottery outcomes often involve a statistical analysis of lottery draw history. While this can yield some potentially useful patterns and trends, the sheer randomness of lottery draws and the enormous dataset present a significant challenge.

AI, on the other hand, can handle this vast amount of information, identifying subtle patterns that might be overlooked by human analysis. Machine learning algorithms can be trained to recognize these patterns and make predictions based on this learned understanding. Moreover, AI's real-time processing capability can adjust these predictions as new data comes in, making the system more adaptable and dynamic.

However, the application of AI in lottery prediction also raises questions regarding fairness, legality, and ethical use of technology. It's crucial to enforce stringent regulations to ensure responsible use of such technologies, preventing manipulation or misuse.

Furthermore, while AI can potentially increase the odds of winning, it cannot override the inherent randomness of lottery draws. The unpredictability and chance factors in the lottery remain, making it impossible to guarantee a win. Thus, while AI might bring a new dimension to the lottery game, it's important to remember that at the end of the day, it remains a game of chance.

In contrast to the inherently random nature of lottery draws, AI predictive analytics can potentially tilt the odds slightly in favor of the player. Machine learning algorithms can be trained on vast amounts of historical lottery draw data, enabling them to detect hidden patterns that may escape human analysis. These patterns, when extrapolated into future draws, can provide more informed predictions, thus improving a player's chances of selecting the correct numbers. However, it is crucial to understand that this doesn't guarantee a win. It merely increases the probability of winning based on historical trends. AI predictive analytics is an insightful tool, but the element of chance inherent to lottery games remains a dominant factor.

As we delve further into the nuances of AI in lottery prediction, we've explored its potential advantages, limitations, and ethical concerns. We've highlighted that while AI can offer a new perspective and perhaps even a slight edge, the inherent randomness of the lottery ensures it remains a game of chance. Now, as we transition into the next chapter, we will shift our focus from the theoretical and into the practical realm.

Chapter 3: Unraveling the Complexity of the Lottery

I n this chapter, we delve into the intricate details of the lottery, a game that seems simple on the surface but hides layers of complexity beneath. We will explore the mathematical principles that govern it and shed light on the randomness and unpredictability that underpin every draw. Though the lottery is often viewed as a straightforward game of luck, understanding its complexity can provide valuable insight into why it has proven so resistant to prediction, even in the era of advanced AI technologies. Let's embark on this journey to unravel the intricacies of the lottery, its workings, and the elusive randomness that makes it both enticing and elusive for prediction models.

Understanding Different Lottery Systems

LOTTERY SYSTEMS AROUND the world vary in their structure and rules but share the common element of randomness. Primarily, there are two types of systems: fixed-odds lotteries and number lotteries.

Fixed-odds lotteries have predetermined odds regardless of how many people participate. In such a system, you select a set of numbers and if those match the drawn numbers, you win. The prize is a fixed amount.

On the other hand, number lotteries, like Powerball or Mega Millions, involve players selecting a set of numbers from a larger pool. In these systems, the jackpot grows each time it's not won, thus the potential rewards can be immense.

Analyzing these systems in an attempt to predict winning numbers involves assessing historical data and identifying any recurring patterns. However, it's important to remember that these systems are designed to be random and unpredictable. AI can be used to analyze past draws, but it's crucial to bear in mind that past patterns do not guarantee future results. Each draw is independent, and the probability of winning remains constant.

While AI can potentially enhance the strategic element of playing the lottery by identifying patterns in the number draws, it's still fundamentally a game of chance. A detailed understanding of the lottery system and its innate randomness is fundamental for anyone hoping to employ AI as a tool in playing the lottery.

Delving Into the Mathematics of Lotteries

THE MATHEMATICAL FRAMEWORK underlying lottery games is rooted in the principles of probability and combinations. In number lotteries, the odds of winning are determined by the total number of potential combinations. For instance, in a lottery where you select six numbers from a pool of 49, the total number of possible combinations would be approximately 14 million, rendering the odds of a single ticket winning incredibly slim.

However, some players and AI systems attempt to defy these odds by examining historical lottery data for patterns. This may involve applying sophisticated statistical techniques to determine if certain numbers appear more frequently than others, or if there are patterns in the occurrence of 'hot' (frequently drawn) and 'cold' (infrequently drawn) numbers. Yet, it's critical to reiterate that each lottery draw is an independent event, and past results do not influence future outcomes.

Some AI systems might employ machine learning algorithms to analyze historical data, creating predictive models that attempt to forecast future results. However, the random nature of lotteries presents a significant challenge to the effectiveness of these models. While AI can provide insights and identify patterns that may not be immediately apparent, it cannot alter the fundamental probabilities of the game. Thus, despite the employment of sophisticated technology, the lottery remains a game of chance, and winning, for the most part, is a matter of luck.

Contrary to the traditional understanding, some argue that AI can indeed be a game-changer in predicting lottery outcomes. The strength of AI lies in its ability to process vast quantities of data rapidly and identify subtle patterns that might elude human analysis. AI, especially machine learning, thrives on information. The more data it has, the better it can learn, adapt, and predict. In the context of lotteries, using historical data spanning decades, AI may discern trends or cycles that seem random or nonsensical to us. These patterns could potentially be used to predict which numbers are more likely to appear in future draws.

Moreover, advanced AI systems can use deep learning algorithms to simulate millions of lottery draws in a short period. This "brute force" method can unearth specific patterns or trends that could potentially increase the odds of winning. However, it's essential to remember that even if AI can improve your chances, it doesn't guarantee a win.

Analyzing and Winning the Lottery: A Data-Driven Approach

IN THE ARENA OF LOTTERY analysis and prediction, there exist several types of games that pose different challenges for data scientists and AI. The standard lottery draw involves picking a set of numbers from a larger pool, typically with a bonus number or "powerball." This form of lottery, with its vast number of possibilities, provides a rich dataset for AI algorithms to analyze.

The challenge is compounded in multi-state or national lotteries, where the pool of numbers and the number of participants increase. Such lotteries generate enormous datasets that, when processed through AI and machine learning algorithms, could potentially reveal patterns or trends that may give players a slight edge.

Another intriguing area of study is instant win games or "scratch-offs." These games, unlike traditional lotteries, provide instant results and are generally considered to be games of pure chance. However, some researchers argue that a data-driven approach might reveal subtle biases in the creation of these games, offering another potential (though still minimal) advantage to the player.

Despite the potential promises of machine learning and AI in lottery prediction, the reality is that these methods may only slightly improve one's chances of winning. It is vital to remember that lotteries are fundamentally games of chance, designed with randomness at their core. No AI or algorithm can guarantee a win, and responsible play should always be the priority.

The Science of Probability in Lottery Winning

IT IS A COMMON MISPERCEPTION that analyzing past lottery results can lead to a winning strategy. Historically, players have tried to predict lottery outcomes based on the frequency of certain numbers or combinations of numbers. However, each lottery draw is independent and random, meaning that past results have no influence on future draws.

In the realm of artificial intelligence, machine learning models have been deployed to find patterns in complex lottery data sets. AI can perform a high-speed, high-volume analysis of past lottery results in an attempt to predict future outcomes. But while these models might be able to identify some repeating patterns, it is important to note that this does not guarantee any future outcome.

The area where AI holds potential is in identifying anomalies or biases in the process of lottery number generation. If any such bias existed, it could be exploited to increase the odds of winning. However, lottery organizations utilize robust random number generation mechanisms to minimize any such potential bias.

While AI cannot guarantee a lottery win, it can potentially assist in uncovering biases, pushing the odds subtly in the player's favor. Machine learning algorithms can analyze massive datasets of past lottery results, looking for irregularities or patterns that may indicate a bias in the random number generation process. For example, if a specific number appears more frequently than would be expected in a truly random process, this could suggest a bias in the number generation algorithm. Once detected, these biases can be strategically exploited; players could, theoretically, adjust their number selection based on these findings. However, it is crucial to emphasize that even if such biases exist, exploiting them would only slightly improve the odds of winning. More importantly, lotteries continually refine their number generation algorithms to eliminate any biases, making it a continual race between the AI detecting biases and lottery organizations eradicating them.

Security Measures in Lottery Systems

LOTTERY ORGANIZATIONS employ stringent security measures to ensure the integrity and fairness of their games. Some of these measures include the use of sophisticated random number generation algorithms, rigorous testing for biases and anomalies, and independent auditing. To further fortify their systems against potential exploitation, these organizations often employ cryptographically secure pseudorandom number generators (CSPRNGs). CSPRNGs are algorithms for generating sequences of numbers that approximate true randomness and are resilient to prediction or manipulation. Moreover, these systems are designed to be immune to reverse-engineering, making it extremely difficult, if not impossible, for even the most sophisticated AI to predict the outcomes. This continual evolution and hardening of lottery systems ensure they stay one step ahead of any attempts to undermine their randomness, further emphasizing the limitations of AI in predicting lottery outcomes.

The Role of Luck in Lottery Outcomes

DESPITE THE TECHNOLOGICAL advancements in AI and the theoretical possibility of identifying number biases, the concept of "luck" remains central to lottery games. Due to the inherent randomness of lottery draws, the majority of outcomes fall under the domain of chance, rather than predictable patterns. In this context, "luck" can be best understood as the favorable alignment of random factors beyond an individual's control or prediction. For lottery participants, it's this element of chance - the possibility of an unlikely event occurring in their favor - that adds an intriguing allure to the game. While AI can potentially improve the odds, the unpredictable nature of these games underscores the fact that winning the lottery is, at its core, a matter of luck. This realization not only demystifies the process but also emphasizes the importance of responsible participation, underscoring that lotteries are forms of entertainment rather than reliable sources of income.

Understanding Random Number Generation

RANDOM NUMBER GENERATION (RNG) is a fundamental aspect of lottery systems, serving as the bedrock of their unpredictability. RNG is a computational or physical process that generates a sequence of numbers or symbols that cannot be reasonably predicted better than by random chance. In the context of lotteries,

RNG is used to determine the winning numbers in each draw, ensuring equal probability for every number combination.

Two main types of RNG exist: True Random Number Generators (TRNGs) and Pseudorandom Number Generators (PRNGs). TRNGs generate numbers from a physical process, such as radioactive decay. They are not predictable and do not follow a distinct pattern. On the other hand, PRNGs generate sequences of numbers that only appear random but are initiated from an initial value called a seed. While PRNGs might seem random to the untrained observer, a person with knowledge of the seed and the algorithm used could predict future numbers in the sequence.

In the lottery system, TRNGs are often preferred due to their unpredictable nature. This ensures the fairness of the lottery draw, contributing to the element of luck that remains central to its appeal. Despite the sophistication and capabilities of current AI technologies, accurately predicting the outcomes of a TRNG-based lottery system remains a formidable challenge, further emphasizing the boundaries of AI applicability in predicting lottery outcomes.

Regulatory Oversight in Lottery Operations

REGULATORY BODIES PLAY a critical role in ensuring the fairness, transparency, and legality of lotteries. Typically, these entities establish and enforce rules around lottery operations, including the use of random number generators, prize allocation, and the handling of ticket sales. They also maintain stringent standards to protect participants from fraudulent activities and ensure that the lottery system remains inviolable.

Moreover, lottery regulators are tasked with upholding ethical and legal standards in the application of AI and other advanced technologies. As AI becomes increasingly prevalent, questions around its application in predicting lottery outcomes necessitate robust discussion and regulation. Regulatory bodies must grapple with the technological capabilities of AI, the mathematical complexities of random events, and their implications for lottery outcomes.

The balance between the use of AI for pattern detection and the principle of chance inherent in lotteries presents a unique challenge for regulators. They must ensure this balance does not tilt in a manner that compromises the integrity of the lottery system, undermines public trust, or violates legal norms. Regulatory bodies, therefore, stand at the intersection of technology, law, and ethics in the context of lotteries, holding the responsibility to navigate this complex terrain.

The Menace of Lottery Scams

LOTTERY SCAMS REPRESENT a significant and growing issue worldwide. Fraudsters prey on the hope and trust of individuals with promises of easy winnings, often resulting in severe financial loss for the victims. These scams typically involve deceptive messages via email, phone call, or letter claiming that the recipient has won a substantial lottery prize. The catch lies in the requirement for the 'winner' to pay a fee or provide personal details to claim the prize, a telltale sign of fraud.

The sophistication of lottery scams has been amplified with the advent of technology, allowing scammers to mask their identities and operate from any part of the world, making it difficult for law enforcement agencies to trace and penalize offenders. The proliferation of such scams has led to a loss of public trust in legitimate lottery operations, posing a critical challenge for regulatory bodies.

These factors underscore the importance of vigilance and public awareness in counteracting lottery scams. Continuous education about recognizing and reporting potential scams, coupled with robust cybersecurity measures and stringent regulations, can play a significant role in curbing this menace. It is equally crucial for regulatory bodies to engage in international cooperation and information sharing to tackle this issue effectively.

The Role of Artificial Intelligence in Predicting Lottery Outcomes

ARTIFICIAL INTELLIGENCE (AI) introduces a paradigm shift in our approach to predicting lottery outcomes, blurring the line between chance and calculable probability. At its core, the lottery is a game of randomness, with each draw designed to be an independent, unpredictable event. Traditional mathematical approaches, while capable of calculating odds, fail to predict specific outcomes due to the inherently random nature of the game.

However, AI, with its vast capabilities in analyzing and learning from large datasets, presents a new angle to this challenge. It employs complex algorithms and machine learning techniques to detect subtle patterns and correlations within seemingly random data. The idea is not to eliminate randomness, but to identify tendencies, however slight, that might indicate a higher probability of certain outcomes.

Yet, the practical application of AI in predicting lottery outcomes isn't without its caveats. There are ethical and legal considerations, such as fairness and the potential use of predictive technology in fraudulent activities. It also raises questions about the impact on the lottery's allure - the thrill of chance and unpredictability.

While some real-world experiments have attempted to use AI for this purpose, the results vary and are dependent on numerous factors. This endeavor, at its current stage, is still largely experimental and speculative. As AI technology continues to evolve, its potential use in this context will be an area of considerable interest and scrutiny.

As we delve deeper into the realm of AI and its unprecedented capabilities, it becomes imperative to dissect its relationship with probability theory. Probability theory, the branch of mathematics that deals with randomness and the likelihood of a specific event's occurrence, forms the bedrock of our understanding of random events such as lottery draws. AI, on the other hand, thrives on data — seeking patterns, learning from them, and adapting its algorithms accordingly.

This next chapter will present an exploration of the fascinating intersection between these two seemingly disparate domains, shedding light on how AI leverages probability theory to decipher the complex, random patterns inherent to lottery outcomes.

Chapter 4: Intersection of AI and Probability Theory

I n this chapter, we delve into the intriguing intersection of Artificial Intelligence and Probability Theory. These two complex systems, when brought together, create a profound paradigm for understanding and possibly predicting random events such as lottery outcomes. Probability theory, a branch of mathematics that quantifies the likelihood of events, forms the foundation for decoding randomness. On the other hand, AI, with its sophisticated algorithms and learning models, consumes and analyzes massive datasets, extracting patterns and learning from them. This chapter aims to unravel the mystery lying at the intersection of these two worlds, providing a detailed examination of how AI applies probability theory to unearth the hidden patterns in random events, as exemplified by lottery outcomes. Be prepared as we embark on this exciting journey, exploring the boundaries of what AI can predict.

Understanding Probability Theory

PROBABILITY THEORY is a fundamental mathematical framework that encompasses the analysis and interpretation of randomness. It is a tool that quantifies uncertainty, offering a mathematical means to study and predict the likelihood of various outcomes. At the heart of probability theory lies the concept of an 'event'—a specific outcome or combination of outcomes from a random phenomenon. The probability of an event is expressed as a number between 0 and 1. A probability of 0 indicates the event will not occur, while a probability of 1 guarantees its occurrence. Between these two extremes lies a multitude of possible probabilities, reflecting degrees of certainty or uncertainty about the event's occurrence. Probability theory builds upon these basics using more complex mathematical structures and principles such as conditional probability, probability distributions, and random variables, serving as a foundation for statistical analysis and inference. In the context of lottery predictions, each draw represents a random event, and understanding the probability of different combinations of numbers being drawn is a fundamental part of the prediction challenge.

AI and Probability Theory

ARTIFICIAL INTELLIGENCE (AI) leverages the principles of probability theory to navigate the vast and complex world of data. AI algorithms, particularly those rooted in machine learning, use probability distributions to capture the inherent randomness and uncertainty in data. They make predictions based on patterns discerned from historical data, assigning probabilities to potential outcomes.

In the context of lottery predictions, an AI system would analyze previous lottery draws, treating each as a unique event with its own probability distribution. This massive historical dataset serves as the training ground for the AI, enabling it to learn the subtle, underlying patterns that might govern these seemingly random events.

However, it's important to remember that while AI is a powerful tool, it is not infallible. The predictions it makes are based on the data it's trained on, and while it can provide probabilities for future lottery outcomes, it cannot guarantee them. As such, the use of AI in lottery predictions should be approached with a clear understanding of its capabilities and limitations.

The Intersection of AI, Probability, and Statistics in Predicting Lottery Outcomes

AI MAKES USE OF PROBABILITY and statistics in several ways. Fundamentally, it uses probability theory to manage uncertainty and make predictions. In machine learning, a subset of AI, algorithms often use statistical principles to learn patterns from data, employing techniques like regression analysis, hypothesis testing, and Bayesian inference. These techniques help the algorithm to understand the variability in the data and estimate the likelihood of different outcomes.

When it comes to predicting lottery outcomes, AI would employ these principles in a specific manner. An AI system would scrutinize historical lottery data, identifying patterns, and correlations. Since each lottery draw is a distinct event with its own probability, the AI would have to consider each possible combination's likelihood, essentially managing a vast amount of probabilistic information.

For instance, a machine learning model might use Bayesian inference to update the probability of a certain lottery number being drawn, based on its frequency in the historical data. Through such a process, the AI could potentially identify patterns or tendencies that are not immediately apparent to the human eye. However, it's worth reiterating that the inherent randomness in lottery draws presents a significant challenge, even for advanced AI. Therefore, any predictions made by such systems should be viewed as probabilistic estimates rather than certain outcomes.

AI in Predictive Modeling

THE USE OF AI IN PREDICTIVE modeling for lotteries is a field marred by as much intrigue as skepticism. The primary approach would be to feed the AI system with vast amounts of historical lottery data. This system, powered by machine learning algorithms, would then process this data, attempting to find patterns or correlations that may indicate a higher probability of certain outcomes.

However, the question that looms large is whether real, meaningful patterns can actually be detected in what is essentially a random event. Some argue that the inherent randomness of a lottery draw makes it impossible for any AI, no matter how advanced, to make accurate predictions. They suggest that any perceived patterns in the data are merely coincidental, an artifact of the human tendency to seek patterns in chaos.

On the other hand, proponents of the use of AI in lottery prediction argue that while the outcomes are random, they are not without a certain degree of predictability. They contend that while the next draw's exact outcome cannot be predicted with certainty, the likelihood of certain outcomes can be estimated using complex AI algorithms. This perspective hinges on the belief that AI's power lies in its ability to process and analyze large volumes of data far beyond human capabilities, potentially uncovering patterns or tendencies that may not be visible at a surface level.

However, even if this were possible, the ethical and legal implications of employing AI to predict lottery outcomes cannot be ignored. Would it be fair to other players if AI were used in this way? Would it be legal? These questions underscore the need for careful, considered discussions on the use of AI in predictive modeling for lotteries.

The Intricacy of Bayesian Networks in Lottery Prediction

BAYESIAN NETWORKS, also known as belief networks, are a type of probabilistic graphical model that uses a directed acyclic graph (DAG) to represent a set of variables and their conditional dependencies. In the context of lottery prediction, the Bayesian network represents the complex, interrelated variables that might influence the outcome of a lottery draw.

Each node in the network represents a variable of interest, such as the outcomes of previous draws, the time and location of the draw, and other potentially influential factors. The edges in the graph represent the conditional dependencies between these variables, indicating how changes in one variable may influence others.

The strength of Bayesian networks lies in their ability to calculate the probabilities of different outcomes based on the known states of the variables represented in the network. This makes them a potentially powerful tool for lottery prediction, as they can estimate the likelihood of different outcomes based on the available data.

However, the effectiveness of Bayesian networks in predicting lottery outcomes is still a matter of debate. Critics argue that the inherent randomness of lottery draws makes it impossible to establish meaningful dependencies between variables. On the other hand, advocates of the method argue that patterns may be discernible in the data when viewed through the lens of a Bayesian network. Nevertheless, even if Bayesian networks could offer some degree of predictive power, the ethical and legal implications of using such methods for lottery prediction must be carefully considered.

Predictive Capabilities: Supervised versus Unsupervised Learning

IN THE REALM OF MACHINE learning, Supervised and Unsupervised Learning represent contrasting but complementary approaches towards data analysis. Their utility in predicting lottery outcomes is an intriguing point of discussion. Supervised learning, which works on labeled data, could potentially be used to train a model based on past lottery results. The model could then predict future outcomes based on patterns it discerned during the training phase.

However, the inherent randomness of lotteries challenges the efficacy of this approach.

Conversely, Unsupervised Learning, which deals with unlabeled data, can be used to cluster lottery results into different groups based on shared characteristics. This approach does not aim to predict specific outcomes but could reveal patterns or structures in the data that are not immediately apparent. For instance, it might identify clusters of similar draw outcomes that occur under certain conditions. This information could potentially be used to inform betting strategies, although its practical utility is yet to be definitively proven.

Regardless of their theoretical capabilities, the use of Supervised and Unsupervised Learning for lottery prediction raises a multitude of questions. These range from technical challenges, such as overfitting and the curse of dimensionality, to ethical considerations about the fairness of using such methods. Moreover, there are legal ramifications to consider, particularly in jurisdictions where lottery prediction is prohibited by law. Consequently, the use of AI in this context must be approached with caution and a clear understanding of the potential risks and rewards.

The Significance of Data Quality and Quantity

THE QUALITY AND QUANTITY of data are crucial in determining the efficacy of AI in making accurate predictions. High-quality data that is representative, unbiased, and devoid of anomalies ensures that the model is trained on a robust and reliable dataset. This, in turn, enhances the model's ability to identify patterns and make accurate predictions. When it comes to lottery predictions, the data must include all possible variables that could influence the outcome.

The quantity of data is equally significant. AI thrives on vast datasets, as the more data it has to learn from, the better its predictive capabilities become. In the context of lottery outcomes, this would mean compiling as many past results as possible. The vastness of the dataset would enable the AI to discern patterns, if they exist, across an extensive range of draws.

Data is the foundation of any AI system. Without it, the AI lacks the necessary training ground to learn and improve. But it's not just about having data; it's about having the right data. Therefore, the process of data collection, cleaning, and processing becomes fundamental in this scenario, making it an important aspect to consider when discussing AI's capabilities in predicting lottery outcomes.

Understanding AI's Decision-Making Processes

AI'S DECISION-MAKING process is fundamentally guided by the algorithms it operates on, which are designed to identify patterns, make complex calculations, and derive predictions. In the context of lottery predictions, AI would leverage algorithms to analyze the historical data of lottery draws, identify any possible patterns or trends, and then predict future outcomes based on these patterns. It's important to note that while these algorithms are sophisticated and intelligent, they are not capable of guaranteeing exact outcomes due to the inherent randomness of lottery draws.

The decision-making process of AI can be seen as a combination of its learning phase and the application of learned patterns. During the learning phase, AI is fed large quantities of data and uses this to adjust its internal parameters, improving the accuracy of its predictions. In the application phase, the AI applies the learned patterns to new data to make predictions. These predictions, however, are probabilities based on patterns found in past data, and not certain outcomes.

In essence, the decision-making process in AI, particularly in context of lottery predictions, is a complex interplay between data analysis, pattern recognition, probability calculation, and learning from previous iterations. While the capability of AI to analyze vast datasets and identify complex patterns is remarkable, it remains a tool to aid in decision-making and not a foolproof solution to lottery predictions.

Risks and Uncertainties in AI-Based Predictions

WHILE AI'S CAPABILITIES in pattern detection and data analysis are impressive, the task of accurately predicting lottery outcomes is fraught with uncertainties. Because lottery draws are fundamentally random events, there is a limit to the accuracy that can be achieved, regardless of the sophistication of the algorithms in use. The inherent randomness means that patterns identified in historical data may not necessarily continue into the future. This unpredictability injects a degree of risk and uncertainty into the AI's predictions.

Moreover, the legal and ethical implications of using AI in this context cannot be ignored. On a legal front, the use of AI for lottery predictions may be considered a violation of the principles of fair play and could potentially lead to legal consequences. Ethically, the deployment of AI for such purposes raises questions about responsible innovation and the potential for exploitation of vulnerable populations.

In conclusion, while the use of AI for lottery predictions is theoretically possible, it is beset by practical challenges and ethical concerns that make it a complex and contentious issue.

The Unpredictability of Randomness: AI's Limitations in Stochastic Environments

IN A STOCHASTIC ENVIRONMENT, characterized by an inherent level of randomness and unpredictability, the capabilities of

AI are significantly restrained. Despite the mathematical prowess that AI possesses, it is fundamentally incapable of predicting random events with absolute certainty. Instead, it operates on the basis of probability and extrapolation from historical data, which can often be misleading in the context of purely random events like lottery draws.

The concept of `randomness` in mathematics is one that is essentially intractable, defying any attempt to pin it down to a predictable pattern or sequence. Even with the most sophisticated machine learning algorithms, an AI system can only analyze past patterns and attempt to extrapolate these into the future. In a stochastic environment, however, these patterns may not hold true, leading to erroneous predictions.

The limitations of AI in such contexts are a sobering reminder of the boundaries of technology. While AI is undoubtedly a powerful tool that can analyze complex datasets and identify hidden patterns with a degree of accuracy unthinkable for human analysts, it remains subject to the fundamental laws of probability and randomness. Therefore, its utility in areas such as lottery prediction remains questionable, and it is essential for those employing these systems to remain aware of their limitations and act responsibly.

Harnessing AI in Predictive Analytics: Exploring Real-World Cases

WHILE THE THEORETICAL limitations of AI in predicting random events are well-established, practical attempts have been made, providing valuable insight into AI's potential and pitfalls in predictive analytics. One such attempt is the use of AI in the stock market. Stock prices, like lottery outcomes, are influenced by a multitude of unpredictable factors. AI algorithms are used to analyze historical data, trading volumes, market sentiment, and other relevant variables to make predictions. However, these predictions are not foolproof and investors are constantly reminded about the inherent risk and unpredictability.

Another interesting case is the use of AI in weather forecasting. Weather patterns, although possessing a degree of randomness, do exhibit cyclical trends and patterns. AI algorithms, leveraging vast datasets, are used to predict these patterns to some extent. The success rate, although not perfect, is significantly higher than random predictions, demonstrating that under certain conditions, AI can provide valuable predictive insights.

These cases illustrate AI's potential in predictive analytics, despite its limitations in environments with high degrees of randomness. They serve as reminders that while AI can't guarantee accurate predictions, it can increase the odds of prediction success, as long as the inherent uncertainties are acknowledged and accounted for. The key lies in understanding and respecting AI's capabilities and limitations, using it as a tool to supplement, not replace, human judgment and expertise.

Chapter 5: Theoretical Application of AI in Lotteries

In Chapter 5, we delve deeper into the theoretical application of artificial intelligence in predicting lottery outcomes - a task that presents an intriguing interplay between randomness and pattern recognition. Drawing parallels from our previous discussions on the use of AI in stock market predictions and weather forecasting, we will explore the mathematical complexities inherent in lottery systems, the potential role of AI in deciphering these complexities, and the ethical and legal implications of such an endeavor. It is essential to bear in mind that, much like our other examples, using AI in this context does not aim to replace human judgment, but rather to augment it. Although the lottery, by design, is a game of chance, this chapter is dedicated to contemplating whether AI's capabilities in pattern detection and predictive analytics can tilt the odds, even if slightly, in favor of predictability.

Feasibility of Predicting Lottery Outcomes with AI

AT FIRST GLANCE, THE idea of predicting lottery outcomes – events that epitomize randomness – with AI might seem implausible. The nature of lottery draws, which are designed to be unpredictable and governed by chance, appears to defy the logic of pattern-based learning and prediction, which is the cornerstone of AI. However, AI's strength lies in its ability to digest and analyze vast datasets to identify subtle, hidden patterns that might not be discernible to humans.

In the context of lotteries, could this mean detecting patterns in the sequence of winning numbers over time, even if they appear random? To answer this, we need to unpack the concept of randomness. In mathematics, a sequence of numbers is considered random if it does not exhibit any identifiable pattern or regularity. However, this does not mean that patterns cannot exist within randomness, especially in finite datasets.

From an AI perspective, the question is not whether a pattern exists, but whether the pattern is useful for prediction. In this regard, AI's ability to predict lottery outcomes would depend heavily on the quality and extent of data fed into it.

However, it's important to note that even if AI could identify and leverage patterns in lottery data to make predictions, this would not guarantee winning results. Instead, it could potentially increase the odds of predicting winning numbers, albeit marginally. This is because, despite AI's formidable analytical abilities, it cannot alter the inherently random nature of lottery draws.

Last but not the least, the ethical and legal implications of using AI to predict lottery outcomes need to be considered. While it could be viewed as an innovative application of technology, there are potential risks related to fairness and legality that must be acknowledged.

Data Mining and Analysis for Lotteries

DATA MINING AND ANALYSIS for lotteries involves the extraction of patterns from historical lottery data using techniques such as statistical analysis, machine learning, and database systems. This process is not as simple as it sounds, considering the massive volumes of data that lotteries generate over time. The data typically includes the winning numbers of every draw, the dates of the draws, and sometimes, additional information such as the number of winners for each draw.

In data mining, various algorithms are employed to analyze this data and to uncover hidden patterns or associations. For example, an algorithm might identify that certain numbers appear more frequently together in winning combinations. Tools like regression analysis, clustering, and neural networks are commonly used in this process.

However, the big question remains - can these patterns be used to predict future outcomes? The answer lies in the concept of predictive analysis, a branch of data mining. Predictive analysis uses historical data to make predictions about the future by identifying trends, patterns, and relationships within the data.

In the context of lotteries, predictive analysis might reveal trends or patterns that could be used to make educated guesses about future outcomes. However, as previously stated, the inherently random nature of lottery draws means that while these predictions might increase the odds of choosing winning numbers, they do not guarantee a win.

Lastly, it is important to underscore the need for responsible data mining practices. Despite its potential benefits, inappropriate use of data mining and analysis in lotteries could lead to unfair advantages and legal consequences. Therefore, caution and ethical considerations are paramount in employing such techniques.

Exploring AI Models for Lottery Prediction

TO DELVE DEEPER INTO the potential of AI for lottery prediction, we must consider the various models that could be employed. One of the most promising is the application of machine learning (ML), a subset of AI that focuses on developing algorithms capable of learning and making decisions without being explicitly programmed.

ML operates on the fundamental premise that machines can learn from data and adapt their operations accordingly. For lottery prediction, ML models would be trained on extensive historical lottery data, learning patterns, trends, and relationships in this data. These could include number frequency, common combinations, or timing of the draws.

One prominent ML model suitable for this task is the neural network. Its structure, inspired by the human brain, enables it to recognize complex patterns within the data. Another ML model that could be used is the decision tree, which makes predictions based on a series of decisions or rules derived from the data.

Notably, the performance of these models is dependent on the quality and quantity of the data used for training. As such, careful data preparation, including cleaning and normalization, is crucial for effective prediction.

However, it is crucial to note that while ML models may increase the probability of predicting more winning numbers, they do not guarantee a win. The element of chance in lotteries still plays a significant role and cannot be completely eliminated through AI or ML. Furthermore, the use of these technologies should always adhere to ethical guidelines to prevent misuse and ensure fair play.

In conclusion, while AI and ML present promising avenues for lottery prediction, their use requires careful consideration of technical, ethical, and legal aspects. Responsible innovation and the understanding that AI should not replace human decision-making are vital to ensure the ethical and effective use of these technologies in predicting lottery outcomes. So, it is essential to continue exploring this topic with a critical lens, keeping in mind both its potential benefits and challenges. Ultimately, responsible and informed use of AI in lottery prediction could lead to more accurate outcomes and potentially reduce the negative impacts of gambling addiction on individuals and society as a whole. Therefore, it is crucial for further research and discussions on this topic to take place, considering all perspectives involved. Including diverse stakeholders such as experts from various fields, policymakers, and affected communities will be necessary for creating comprehensive guidelines and regulations for the responsible application of AI in lotteries. By doing so, we can harness the power of AI for more accurate predictions while ensuring fair play and responsible innovation. As technology continues to advance, ongoing evaluation and adaptation will also be necessary to keep up with any new developments and challenges that may arise. In summary, the use of AI in lottery prediction is a complex topic that requires careful consideration and responsible application for potential benefits to be realized while minimizing any potential negative impacts on society. So, let's continue exploring this fascinating intersection between technology and chance with a critical yet open mind. Let us pave the way towards a future where ethical and effective use of AI helps make life-changing dreams come true for individuals without compromising fairness or causing harm to others. #

In recent years, there has been a growing interest in the use of AI to predict lottery outcomes. This has sparked debates and discussions around the potential benefits and drawbacks of such an approach. While some argue that AI could improve accuracy and potentially reduce issues like fraud, others raise concerns about the implications for fairness, responsible gambling, and privacy. As with any new technology, it is essential to take a critical and informed approach when considering its application in sensitive areas like lotteries.

To understand the complexities of using AI for lottery prediction, we must first recognize that predicting random events is a challenging task mathematically. It involves analyzing vast amounts of data to detect patterns and make accurate predictions. However, even with advanced algorithms and powerful computing capabilities, there are no guarantees when it comes to predicting chance-based events. The very nature of randomness makes it impossible to achieve perfect accuracy.

Moreover, there are practical considerations that must be taken into account when using AI for lottery prediction. This includes issues such as data privacy, algorithm transparency, and potential biases in the training data used by AI systems. Additionally, there are ethical concerns to consider, such as responsible gambling practices and ensuring fairness for all participants in lotteries.

The Power of Neural Networks in Lottery Prediction

NEURAL NETWORKS, A subfield of AI, have demonstrated remarkable predictive capabilities in various domains, from image recognition to stock market analysis. In the context of lottery prediction, they hold significant potential, but it's not without caveats. Neural networks, particularly deep learning models, thrive on vast datasets, learning to identify subtle patterns and correlations that may elude even the most experienced analysts.

In lottery prediction, a neural network could be trained on historical lottery data, learning from the sequences of winning numbers to predict future outcomes. However, as stated earlier, predicting random events like lottery draw outcomes, is inherently challenging. Despite the advanced capabilities of neural networks, they are still bound by the intrinsic unpredictability of these events. The patterns they identify in the training data may not necessarily hold in the future, due to the sheer randomness of lottery draws.

Moreover, the use of neural networks for lottery prediction raises the same practical, ethical, and legal questions outlined in previous sections. Ensuring data privacy, maintaining algorithm transparency, and promoting responsible gambling practices are all critical considerations when employing such powerful technology. In conclusion, while neural networks may offer intriguing possibilities for lottery prediction, their practical use must be approached with caution, considering both their technical limitations and broader implications.

Pattern Recognition and Artificial Intelligence: A Deep Dive

THE CRUX OF AI LIES in pattern recognition, a key element that allows these systems to learn from exposure to data over time. Pattern recognition in this context refers to an AI's ability to identify and categorize data patterns, enabling it to make predictions or decisions without being explicitly programmed to perform the task. This ability to detect patterns is crucial for tasks such as image recognition, natural language processing, and indeed, lottery prediction.

In the case of lottery prediction, the AI would sift through a vast array of historical lottery data, looking for patterns or anomalies that could potentially indicate future outcomes. The principle here is that by understanding the past, we can predict the future. However, given the inherent randomness of lottery draws, this is a tall order. It's essential to remember that even if an AI detects a pattern in past draws, this doesn't guarantee that the pattern will hold in future draws.

Moreover, the use of pattern recognition in AI brings to surface several ethical and legal concerns. As AI systems are fed more data and their pattern recognition skills improve, questions about data privacy and transparency grow. For instance, who owns the patterns that AI systems discover? And what happens if these patterns are used for malicious purposes? These are complex questions that society must grapple with as AI becomes increasingly integrated into our daily lives.

In conclusion, while pattern recognition is a powerful ability of AI, its application in the realm of lottery prediction is fraught with challenges and concerns. As we continue to explore this frontier, it's imperative to proceed with caution and consider the broader implications of our actions.

The Logic and Practicalities of Algorithmic Predictions

WHEN DELVING INTO THE algorithmic predictions of lottery outcomes, it becomes important to understand the logic and practicalities that form the basis for these predictions. At the core of these predictions is the principle of probability. Every lottery draw is a separate event and theoretically, each combination of numbers has an equal chance of being selected. This, in itself, makes prediction a challenging task. Nevertheless, an algorithm that can analyze past data, identifying patterns and frequency of occurrence, may offer a slight advantage, albeit minuscule.

However, the implementation of such an algorithm requires careful consideration. First, the algorithm must be robust enough to analyze vast amounts of data quickly and accurately. Next, it must be adaptable to the dynamic nature of lottery systems, which may vary in rules, number pools, and draw frequencies across different countries or states.

Furthermore, the algorithm needs to consider the randomness factor in lottery draws. While the frequency of a number's occurrence in past draws might be high, it does not increase its likelihood in future draws due to the independent nature of each draw.

To summarize, while the application of AI in lottery predictions presents an interesting theoretical possibility, the practicality of it is heavily influenced by the nature of randomness and the complex, dynamic elements of lottery systems.

A Deep Dive into Synthetic Lottery Draws Simulation

THE SIMULATION OF SYNTHETIC lottery draws is a compelling approach that can enhance the predictive capabilities of AI algorithms. This involves creating a large number of hypothetical lottery draws, leveraging computer-based modeling techniques. The primary advantage of this approach is that it provides a robust dataset, extending beyond the historical records available.

In each synthetic lottery draw, the selection of numbers is random yet corresponds to the rules and parameters of the real-world lottery system being simulated. The outcome of these simulations can offer valuable insights into the frequency and combinations of numbers that could potentially occur in actual draws.

However, one should bear in mind the inherent limitations of these simulations. Despite their sophistication, they are still unable to completely circumvent the fundamental challenge of predicting random events. Synthetic lottery draws can, nonetheless, augment our understanding of patterns and trends in lottery outcomes, thereby equipping AI algorithms with better predictive power.

Ultimately, the practical utility of these simulations in actual lottery prediction should be evaluated cautiously, taking into account their theoretical assumptions and computational underpinnings.

Backtesting: Running Historical Numbers Through AI

BACKTESTING IS A FUNDAMENTAL component in validating the effectiveness of AI-powered lottery prediction models. By running historical lottery numbers through AI algorithms, we can assess the accuracy of their predictive capabilities in a controlled environment. This technique allows us to simulate the model's performance if it had been applied to past lottery draws.

During backtesting, each historical lottery draw is treated as a separate event. The AI model is tasked with generating a prediction for each of these events, based on the data available prior to that particular draw. The predicted results are then compared with the actual outcomes, providing a practical measure of the model's precision.

This process is crucial in highlighting any potential weaknesses in the AI model, such as overfitting, where the model might perform exceptionally well on the training data but fails to generalize effectively on unseen, real-world data. On the other hand, underfitting can also be identified, signifying that the model is too simplistic to capture the underlying complexities of the lottery system.

However, despite its importance, backtesting has its own limitations. It assumes that the future will behave like the past, which is not always accurate especially for random events like lottery draws. Therefore, while backtesting is an integral part of model validation, its results should be interpreted cautiously. As always, the aim is not to guarantee exact predictions, but to develop AI models that can identify patterns and trends with an acceptable level of reliability.

Evaluating the Predictive Power of AI in Lottery Systems

IN THE LIGHT OF DETERMINING the effectiveness of AI models in predicting lottery outcomes, it's imperative to understand that the measure of accuracy extends beyond mere comparison between predicted and actual results. A deeper analysis of results necessitates the scrutiny of statistical significance, which provides insight into whether any patterns identified by the AI model occurred by chance or are indicative of an actual underlying structure.

Statistical significance is commonly assessed using hypothesis testing, where a null hypothesis (usually stating that there is no relationship between two measured phenomena) is tested against an alternative hypothesis. In the context of our AI model, the null hypothesis could state that there is no difference between the model's predictions and random chance. If the test results in rejecting the null hypothesis, it would suggest that the patterns identified by the AI are statistically significant, thereby validating the model's predictive power.

Nevertheless, it's crucial to note that statistical significance doesn't necessarily equate to practical significance. Even if a model shows a statistically significant improvement over random chance, the size of this improvement should be substantial enough to justify the use of AI for predicting lottery outcomes. In addition, ethical, legal, and practical considerations also play significant roles in determining the practical significance of using AI in this context. As AI continues to evolve and push boundaries, these considerations are essential for ensuring responsible and sustainable innovation.

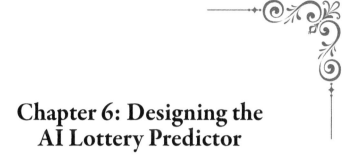

Chapter 6: Designing the AI Lottery Predictor

I n this chapter, we delve into the technical aspects of creating an AI model capable of predicting lottery outcomes. Our journey takes us into the heart of machine learning algorithms, data preprocessing techniques, and strategies for tuning model performance. We will explore the delicate balance between overfitting and underfitting, and how to navigate the challenges that arise in training our model. A robust discussion on the selection of features to be included in the model, and how these features can be processed for optimal results, will also be under scrutiny. As we step into the world of AI model design, let's remember that our goal is not just to create a model that works in theory, but one that is practically significant, ethically acceptable, and legally compliant.

Building the Architectural Framework

IN CONSTRUCTING OUR AI model, the first step involves designing the architectural framework. At this stage, we decide on the structure and components that form the backbone of the model. A neural network, for instance, would necessitate decisions regarding the number of layers and nodes, the activation functions, and the method for error propagation. For more traditional machine learning models, such as regression or decision trees, we would need to determine the form of the function or the splitting criteria, respectively. The architectural design is heavily influenced by the nature of the problem at hand, the data available, and the computational resources at our disposal. However, it is only the starting point in our journey toward building an AI lottery predictor. In the subsequent sections, we will delve into the specifics of data preprocessing, feature selection, and model tuning, all vital components of our AI model design.

Essential Tools and Tech Stack

BEFORE DELVING INTO the specifics of the AI model, it's important to understand the necessary tools and technologies that will form our tech stack. As the foundation of our lottery prediction model, it's crucial that our setup is both robust and versatile. Python, with its plethora of libraries such as TensorFlow and PyTorch for machine learning and deep learning models, is the language of choice for many AI-based projects. Apart from this, data manipulation libraries like Pandas and Numpy, and data visualization libraries like Matplotlib and Seaborn, provide the necessary tools to manage and understand our data. For large-scale data processing and model training, cloud-based solutions like Google's Colab or Microsoft's Azure can provide the necessary computational power. Understanding these tools and how they interact is a fundamental aspect of developing an AI model. In the next section, we will explore how these tools can be utilized in each step of our model's development.

Harnessing Data: Acquiring and Preparing Lottery Datasets

THE FIRST STEP IN ANY data-driven project, especially in the domain of artificial intelligence, is the acquisition of relevant and robust datasets. Lottery outcomes, while seemingly random, are guided by precise mathematical probabilities that can be encapsulated within data. Therefore, to build an AI model capable of predicting lottery outcomes, we must first gather a comprehensive dataset of past lottery results.

Several countries and states publish official lottery results, offering a rich source of data. These datasets can be obtained from the official websites or through an API, if available. It's important to ensure that the data is well-documented and contains results over a significant time period to capture the inherent randomness of lottery outcomes.

Once the data is obtained, the next step is preprocessing, which involves cleaning the data and handling missing or erroneous values. This phase also includes feature selection, which involves identifying the most important data attributes contributing to the prediction outcomes. These attributes can include details such as the date and time of the draw, location of the draw, and type of lottery, among others.

As we proceed through each phase of data gathering and preprocessing, we must maintain rigorous documentation and practice ethical data management, ensuring respect for any privacy laws or guidelines that might apply. This forms the basis of not just our technological endeavor, but also our commitment to responsible innovation.

Lottery Prediction: Machine Learning Models and Techniques

HAVING SUCCESSFULLY obtained and preprocessed your lottery dataset, the next step in crafting an AI model for lottery prediction involves selecting and implementing appropriate machine learning techniques. Often, this requires a decision between supervised or unsupervised learning models. Supervised models, such as regression or decision trees, use known input-output pairs to predict outcomes, while unsupervised models, like clustering or neural networks, identify patterns in the data without prior knowledge of the outcomes.

In the context of lottery prediction, you might consider using time series forecasting models, as lottery results are sequential and time-dependent. Techniques such as ARIMA (AutoRegressive Integrated Moving Average) or LSTM (Long Short-Term Memory) networks, a type of recurrent neural network, can be particularly effective in analyzing time-series data.

Additionally, ensemble methods, which integrate multiple machine learning models to improve prediction performance, can be explored. This approach combines the strengths of various models, reducing the likelihood of error and improving overall prediction reliability.

Remember, the chosen model must be continuously trained and monitored for accuracy over time. Machine learning is not a one-time process but an ongoing one, requiring regular updates to respond to changes in data patterns.

In the next section, we shall delve into these techniques in greater detail, discussing their advantages, limitations, and practical applications in the realm of lottery prediction.

Exploring Machine Learning Algorithms for Lottery Prediction

WHEN IT COMES TO SELECTING the right machine learning algorithm for lottery prediction, there are several factors to consider. The chosen algorithm must be able to effectively handle time-series data, given the sequential nature of lottery results. As previously mentioned, techniques such as ARIMA and LSTM can be particularly useful for this type of data. ARIMA models are renowned for their ability to understand and predict future points in a series that is linearly correlated with past data. On the other hand, LSTM networks, a type of recurrent neural network, are known for their exceptional ability to remember past information and are hence excellent for sequence prediction problems.

Ensemble methods should also be investigated as potential solutions. By integrating multiple models, ensemble methods can leverage the strengths of each model to reduce error likelihood and enhance overall prediction reliability. For instance, a popular ensemble method, Random Forest, operates by constructing multiple decision trees and outputting the mode of the classes for classification or mean prediction for regression.

It is crucial to remember that machine learning is not a one-time process. The selected model requires continuous training and monitoring for accuracy over time. It needs regular updates to respond to changes in data patterns effectively. In the subsequent sections, we will scrutinize the benefits, limitations, and practical applications of these techniques within the context of lottery prediction.

As intimidating as the process might initially seem, implementing machine learning models for lottery prediction follows a series of rational steps. To begin, gather a robust dataset of past lottery results. This data will serve as the training material for the chosen algorithm. The next step involves preprocessing this data, cleaning it to ensure its quality, and reshaping it into a format suitable for the selected machine learning model.

Once the data is ready, choose the appropriate model as discussed previously, and train it with the dataset. This involves feeding the algorithm with the historical lottery data so it can learn the underlying patterns. After training, the model should be tested with a subset of the data not used in the training phase. This helps assess its predictive accuracy and adjust its parameters for better performance.

Implementing ensemble methods involves training multiple models and then combining their outputs in a meaningful way. This could mean averaging the outputs for a regression problem or voting for classification problems.

Bear in mind that the model's performance will inevitably vary over time as data patterns change. As such, regular retraining and updating of the model with fresh data is crucial to maintain its accuracy. The model should also be continually evaluated to ensure it meets the required performance standards. This practice, known as model validation, ensures that the model remains effective and reliable over time. Lastly, always consider the ethical implications of using AI in such contexts, and ensure responsible use of the technology.

Implementing the Model: The Intricacies and Obstacles

IMPLEMENTING A MODEL for predicting lottery outcomes isn't straightforward due to the inherent randomness of lottery draws. However, the process begins with preparing the data for training. This includes cleaning the data, handling missing values, and potentially feature engineering to transform existing variables or create new ones that may improve the model's predictive ability.

Next, the data is split into training and testing datasets. The model is trained on the training data, learning to recognize patterns and make predictions based on these patterns. This phase can be computationally intensive and time-consuming, especially with large datasets and complex models.

Once the model has been trained, it is tested on the test data. This step evaluates the model's performance on previously unseen data, providing a realistic indicator of its predictive accuracy. Various metrics, including precision, recall, and the F1 score, can be used to assess the model's performance.

Despite these technical steps, it's important to remember that predicting lottery outcomes is an inherently uncertain task. It is subject to the laws of chance, and no model can guarantee absolute accuracy.

Therefore, the focus should be on understanding the limitations of these predictive techniques and using them responsibly.

Evaluating Model Accuracy: A Deep Dive into Metrics and Meaning

MODEL EVALUATION IS a crucial step in the AI implementation process. It's through this process that we understand the efficacy of our model in predicting lottery outcomes. The accuracy of a model is not just about how often it predicts winning numbers, but also how it fares when predicting non-winning outcomes. This is determined through a confusion matrix, which provides four measures: true positives, false positives, true negatives, and false negatives.

True positives occur when the model correctly predicts a winning outcome, and true negatives occur when the model correctly predicts a non-winning outcome. False positives and negatives represent incorrect predictions. Together, these measures help calculate precision (the ratio of correctly predicted positive observations to total predicted positives) and recall (the ratio of correctly predicted positive observations to the all observations in actual class).

The F1 score is another crucial metric, providing a balance between precision and recall. It is particularly useful in cases where we have uneven class distribution, as is often the case in lottery prediction — there are typically vastly more non-winning outcomes than winning outcomes.

Even with these measures of accuracy, however, it is essential to remember the inherent unpredictability of lottery outcomes. While the model can identify patterns and probabilities, the actual lottery outcome is ultimately dictated by chance. Therefore, these models should be used with caution and ethical considerations in mind.

Refining the model: Iterative enhancements

THE PROCESS OF REFINING an AI model is an iterative one, involving continual testing and optimization. After an initial model is developed and trained using a subset of the available data, it is then validated and tested using unseen data. This helps to gauge its performance and identify areas where it can be improved. Potential areas of improvement may include hyperparameter tuning, feature engineering, or even the application of different machine learning algorithms.

Furthermore, refining a model for lottery prediction also involves striking a balance between achieving high accuracy and avoiding overfitting. Overfitting occurs when a model is so finely tuned to the training data that it fails to generalize well to new, unseen data. Techniques such as cross-validation, regularization, and ensemble methods can be employed to mitigate this risk.

Lastly, the iterative process of model refinement does not end with the deployment of the model. Real-world application and continuous monitoring can provide valuable data for further model enhancement. This process of constant learning and evolution is what makes AI a powerful tool for understanding complex, stochastic systems like lottery draws. However, as always, the usage of these models must be tempered with ethical considerations and regulatory compliance.

Real-world Testing: Logistics and Compliance

AFTER THE MODEL HAS been initially refined through rigorous testing and iterative enhancements, the next stage involves real-world testing. This phase is crucial in assessing how the model performs under actual operating conditions. One of the key considerations here is the logistical aspect. For instance, how fast can the model process the lottery data? Can it handle the sheer volume of draws that occur worldwide?

Furthermore, compliance with laws and regulations is paramount when implementing this model in the real world. In many jurisdictions, there are stringent rules governing lottery operations, including the use of AI and other predictive technologies. Non-compliance not only has legal repercussions but can also tarnish the reputation of individuals or organizations involved. Therefore, it is essential to consult with legal experts or regulatory authorities to ensure all activities conform to the relevant laws and regulations.

In conclusion, while refining a model for lottery predictions using AI can potentially improve accuracy, it's essential to handle the model ethically and responsibly. Regular monitoring and adjustments, coupled with stringent compliance to laws and providence of a fair playing field for all lottery participants, should be the guiding principles of such an endeavor.

Ensuring Ethical AI: The Responsibility of Predictive Models

IN THE USE OF AI FOR predicting lottery outcomes, securing the model against misuse and ensuring ethical usage is of paramount importance. AI, while a powerful tool, can be subjected to manipulations which may lead to unfair advantages. Therefore, it's essential to implement robust security measures that can prevent unauthorized access and potential misuse.

Additionally, the ethical boundaries surrounding the use of AI in predicting lottery outcomes must be strictly respected. It's vital to remember that while it's technologically feasible to use AI for such purposes, it doesn't necessarily mean it's ethically acceptable to do so. AI models must be designed with fairness and transparency in mind, creating an equal playing field for all participants.

Moreover, the use of AI should not compromise the random nature of lottery draws, which is an integral part of the lottery's appeal and its underlying premise. Tampering with this randomness could lead to a loss of public trust and uproar in the lottery community, potentially leading to legal repercussions.

In conclusion, while AI presents an exciting opportunity in the field of lottery predictions, it's crucial that its implementation is carried out responsibly, with a keen focus on maintaining security and respecting ethical boundaries.

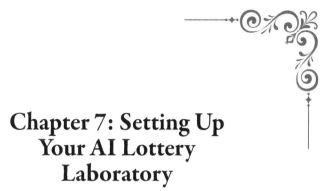

Chapter 7: Setting Up Your AI Lottery Laboratory

As we delve deeper into the complexities and possibilities of predicting lottery outcomes using AI, you might wonder how to set up a platform to experiment with these concepts yourself. Welcome to Chapter 7, "Setting Up Your AI Lottery Laboratory". In this chapter, we'll guide you through the process of building a rudimentary yet functional AI model for lottery prediction. We'll cover the necessary hardware and software requirements, data acquisition and preparation, and the steps to implement the prediction model. As always, we underline the importance of ethical and responsible use of this technology. Let's embark on this exciting journey of creating our own AI lottery laboratory.

Requirements: Hardware and Software

BEFORE WE DELVE INTO the specifics of building an AI model for lottery prediction, it's vital to understand the hardware and software requirements. As with any machine learning project, the complexity of your model will dictate the computational power needed. A basic desktop computer with an i5 or higher processor, 8GB of RAM, and decent hard drive space should be sufficient for a rudimentary model. However, for more complex models that involve deep learning, a high-end computer with a robust GPU, an i7 or higher processor, and at least 16GB of RAM is recommended.

From a software perspective, Python is the language of choice due to its simplicity, versatility, and the plethora of libraries it offers for data analysis and machine learning, such as NumPy, Pandas, TensorFlow, and Scikit-learn. An Integrated Development Environment (IDE) like Jupyter Notebook or Google Colab can also be a useful tool, offering a convenient platform for writing and executing code, data visualization, and documenting your project.

Please note that these are just the basic requirements and may need to be customized based on the specific needs of your project. In the next section, we will delve into the process of data acquisition and preparation. Remember, the success of your AI model heavily depends on the quality and quantity of the data you feed into it.

Acquiring and Preparing Your Data: Key Considerations

FOR ANY AI MODEL, THE first significant step is acquiring and preparing your data. Lottery data, which can be numerical or categorical, is typically available from lottery commission websites or third-party data aggregators. For instance, you can find historical Powerball winning numbers on the official Powerball website: `https://www.powerball.com/`.

To prepare your data, start by cleaning it. This process involves dealing with missing values, duplicates, and erroneous entries. Python's Pandas library provides robust functionality for these tasks. Next, you might need to transform your data. For instance, if your data includes the date of each draw, you can break that down into more relevant features like the day of the week or the month of the draw. This is known as feature engineering.

Remember, this step is iterative; you may need to revisit it based on the performance of your model. For instance, you might discover that a certain feature you initially overlooked has a strong impact on your prediction accuracy. Therefore, keep your original dataset intact and create copies for manipulation. This will allow you to experiment freely and backtrack when necessary.

Understanding the Basics of Programming and Software for AI

PROGRAMMING IS A FUNDAMENTAL skill for implementing AI models. For predicting lottery outcomes, you'll need a robust understanding of a programming language that supports AI model development, such as Python, R, or Julia. Python, particularly, is a popular choice due to its simplicity and the wide range of libraries it provides for machine learning and data analysis, such as TensorFlow, Keras and PyTorch. Beginner programmers can utilize resources like Codecademy (`https://www.codecademy.com/learn/learn-python-3`) or Coursera (`https://www.coursera.org/courses?query=python`) to learn Python.

For software, a suitable integrated development environment (IDE) can be useful. Jupyter Notebook (`https://jupyter.org/`), for instance, is a web-based platform that supports live code, visualizations, and narrative text. It's great for data cleaning, transformation, and model experimentation. Installing Jupyter Notebook along with Python and other useful packages can be easily accomplished through Anaconda (`https://www.anaconda.com/products/distribution`), a free and open-source distribution of Python and R.

Remember, learning to code is a process. Practice regularly, work on projects - such as this lottery prediction model - and don't hesitate to seek help from the vast community of developers available in forums such as Stack Overflow (`https://stackoverflow.com/`).

Ensuring Data Security and Implementing Backup Solutions

IN THE REALM OF AI and data analysis, data security is paramount. It's important to adhere to best practices and regulations to protect sensitive information while processing vast quantities of data. Encryption is a common method of securing data (`https://us.norton.com/internetsecurity-privacy-what-is-data-encryption.html`). Tools like BitLocker (`https://www.microsoft.com/en-us/windows/bitlocker`) and FileVault (`https://support.apple.com/en-us/HT204837`) offer full disk encryption for Windows and MacOS respectively. For a backup solution, consider services like Backblaze (`https://www.backblaze.com/`) or Carbonite (`https://www.carbonite.com/`), which provide automated and secure cloud backups. Open-source solution Duplicati (`https://www.duplicati.com/`) also provides encrypted backups to various cloud storage providers. Remember, data loss can be devastating, especially in AI projects where data is the heart and soul of your model. Regular backups, therefore, are non-negotiable. Always keep your data encrypted, backed up, and secure.

Harnessing Essential Software Applications in AI Projects

TO EFFECTIVELY MANAGE and execute AI projects, a suite of robust software applications is essential. Python has proven to be one of the most popular programming languages for AI because of its simplicity and flexibility. The Python Software Foundation (`https://www.python.org/`) provides an exhaustive repository of resources for learning and mastering Python. For Python development environments, consider using PyCharm (`https://www.jetbrains.com/

pycharm/`), a professional IDE that offers a range of sophisticated features for coding in Python.

For data analysis and visualization, Pandas (`https://pandas.pydata.org/`) and Matplotlib (`https://matplotlib.org/`) are two powerful Python libraries that provide diverse functionality. Pandas excels at data manipulation and analysis, while Matplotlib provides a flexible interface for creating static, animated, and interactive plots in Python.

For developing machine learning models, Scikit-learn (`https://scikit-learn.org/stable/`) is a popular choice, offering a wide range of supervised and unsupervised learning algorithms via a consistent interface in Python. TensorFlow (`https://www.tensorflow.org/`) is another powerful tool for building and training machine learning models.

Remember, the secret to mastering these tools lies in regular practice, so consider working on projects, like our lottery prediction model, to hone your skills.

Ensuring Optimal Networking and Connectivity for AI Projects

IN THE REALM OF AI projects, especially those requiring real-time data analysis such as lottery prediction models, reliable networking and seamless connectivity are crucial. Internet connectivity enables AI systems to access and analyze vast online databases in real-time, and network architecture facilitates data transport and communication among different components of an AI system.

High-speed, dependable internet is a prerequisite for data-intensive tasks like lottery prediction, where delays can significantly impact the accuracy of predictions. Therefore, investing in a robust and reliable internet connection is vital. You may consider service providers like

Comcast   (`https://www.xfinity.com/`)   or   AT&T
(`https://www.att.com/`) who offer high-speed internet services.

For networking, it is beneficial to ensure that all components of
your AI system are interconnected through an efficient network
architecture. This could involve setting up Local Area Networks
(LAN) or Wide Area Networks (WAN) depending on the scale of
your operations. For a comprehensive understanding of network setup,
refer   to   the   Cisco   networking   academy's   guide
(`https://www.netacad.com/courses/packet-tracer`).

Additionally, using cloud-based platforms like Amazon Web
Services   (`https://aws.amazon.com/`)   or   Microsoft   Azure
(`https://azure.microsoft.com/`) can offer scalable storage and
computing power, making them ideal for handling large-scale AI
projects. These platforms also provide numerous AI and machine
learning tools, which can be beneficial in improving the efficiency of
your AI system.

Remember, the success of your AI project greatly depends on a
robust internet and network setup. Regular testing and optimization of
your network architecture can ensure it remains conducive for your AI
operations.

Establishing a Strong Internet and Network Base for AI Systems

THE FIRST STEP TO SETTING up an efficient AI system for
lottery prediction is securing a high-speed internet connection. A
reliable provider like Comcast Comcast[1] or AT&T AT&T[2] can assure
minimized delays crucial for the accuracy of such data-intensive tasks.
The next focal point should be an efficient network architecture,
connecting all components of your AI system. For an in-depth guide

---

1. https://www.xfinity.com/

2. https://www.att.com/

on network setup, visit the Cisco Networking Academy's resource Cisco Networking Academy[3].

Cloud-based platforms come highly recommended for their scalability and computing power, making them indispensable for large-scale AI operations. Platforms like Amazon Web Services Amazon Web Services[4] or Microsoft Azure Microsoft Azure[5] not only offer storage solutions but also provide AI and machine learning tools to enhance system efficiency. A robust network setup forms the backbone of a successful AI project. Regular testing and optimizing your network architecture will ensure it always supports your AI operations.

Addressing Common Problems in AI System Setup

WHEN WORKING WITH COMPLEX technologies like AI, encountering challenges is inevitable. However, understanding these common issues can equip you to address and prevent them effectively. One prevalent problem is insufficient data. AI systems require vast datasets for training and prediction, and the lack of adequate data can severely hinder performance. To remedy this, you could use open-source datasets available on platforms like Kaggle[6] or Google Dataset Search[7].

Another common issue is overfitting, where the AI model learns the training data too well and performs poorly with new, unseen data.

---

3. https://www.netacad.com/courses/packet-tracer

4.   https://aws.amazon.com/

5.   https://azure.microsoft.com/

6. https://www.kaggle.com/datasets

7. https://datasetsearch.research.google.com/

Tools like scikit-learn[8] offer methods to prevent overfitting, such as cross-validation and regularization.

Lastly, ensure that your AI system complies with relevant legal and ethical guidelines. Understanding the legislation around data privacy and AI usage is crucial. Refer to resources like the AI Ethics Guidelines[9] provided by the European Commission.

Remember, troubleshooting is an ongoing process, and keeping up-to-date with the latest technologies and best practices can significantly ease this process. Regular system maintenance and updates will ensure your AI operations run smoothly.

Enhancing AI System Performance: Techniques and Best Practices

OPTIMIZING YOUR AI system setup is integral to achieving accurate, reliable results, particularly in challenging applications like predicting lottery outcomes. One primary strategy involves fine-tuning your system's hyperparameters. Tools such as AutoML[10] can automate this process, making it more efficient and less prone to human error.

Another strategy is feature engineering, which involves selecting or creating the input variables that your model will learn from. Featuretools[11] is an open-source library that automates feature engineering, saving time and helping to uncover complex patterns.

Moreover, upgrading your hardware can provide substantial performance improvements. Implementing a powerful GPU or using cloud-based platforms like Google Colab[12] can significantly accelerate your AI computations.

---

8.   https://scikit-learn.org/

9.   https://ec.europa.eu/digital-single-market/en/news/ethics-guidelines-trustworthy-ai

10. https://cloud.google.com/automl

11.   https://www.featuretools.com/

12.   https://colab.research.google.com/

Remember, optimization is not a one-off process; continuous monitoring and adjustment are necessary to maintain peak performance. Consider setting up a system for tracking your model's performance over time, using platforms like MLflow[13] for end-to-end machine learning lifecycle management. Regular updates and system checks will ensure your AI system performance remains at its best.

The Importance of Regular Maintenance and Updates in AI Systems

KEEPING YOUR AI SYSTEM updated and well-maintained is paramount in the fast-paced world of technology, especially when it comes to predicting complex events like lottery outcomes. Outdated models can lead to ineffective results as they might not account for recent changes or advancements in AI technology.

One essential part of maintenance is ensuring that your AI model is trained with the most recent and relevant data. Data feeds should be regularly updated and checked for quality. Websites like Databricks[14] offer cloud-based platforms for data engineering tasks, ensuring your model is always trained with the most up-to-date information.

Software updates are equally important. Make sure to stay informed about new releases and updates of your AI platform. Platforms like TensorFlow[15] and PyTorch[16] regularly roll out updates that can improve performance, add new features, or fix bugs in the system.

To ensure the longevity of your AI system, consider automating the maintenance and update process. Tools like Nagios[17] can monitor

---

13.   https://mlflow.org/

14.   https://databricks.com/

15.   https://www.tensorflow.org/

16.   https://pytorch.org/

17.   https://www.nagios.org/

your system's performance, alert you about needed updates, and even automate some maintenance tasks. Following these steps will keep your AI system at the forefront of technology, enhancing its performance and accuracy.

Chapter 8: Data Mining for the Lottery

In this chapter, we delve into the fascinating world of data mining in the context of lottery predictions. We focus on the power of data analytics tools and artificial intelligence in sifting through massive data sets to potentially detect valuable patterns and correlations. This process, known as data mining, can be transformative in numerous fields, including the lottery industry, presenting intriguing possibilities and challenges. As we navigate this complex landscape, we will shed light on the methodologies used, the viability of these techniques, and the ethical conundrums they engender. Welcome to the mesmerizing realm of data mining for the lottery.

Understanding the Concept of Data Mining

DATA MINING IS A PROCESS that involves discovering patterns in large data sets through the use of machine learning, statistics, and database systems. It's a crucial part of knowledge discovery in databases (KDD), and it's the step where modeling and inference methods are applied to extract patterns from the data. The ultimate objective of data mining is to extract valuable information from these patterns and use it for further understanding or knowledge generation.

There is an array of data mining techniques available, including clustering, classification, regression, association rules, and anomaly detection. These techniques are designed to handle complex and large sets of data, making data mining an indispensable tool in the era of big data. For hands-on learning, websites like Kaggle[1] and DataCamp[2] provide interactive data science courses and competitions.

In the context of lottery prediction, data mining could be employed to analyze historical lottery data. Although the lottery is a random game of chance, discerning subtle patterns might offer insights into the mechanism behind the seemingly random sequence of winning numbers. To embark on this journey, one can start by gathering past lottery data, cleaning and structuring the data, employing suitable data mining techniques, and analyzing the results. Websites like Lottery Post[3] provide historical lottery data that can be used for this purpose.

Remember, predicting lottery outcomes with high accuracy remains a contentious issue, given the inherent randomness of the game. Nevertheless, the exploration of this concept from a data mining perspective is a fascinating intellectual endeavor that can yield valuable knowledge about the nature of random events and the power (and limitations) of AI and big data.

Decoding the Lottery: AI and Pattern Recognition

USING ARTIFICIAL INTELLIGENCE (AI) to analyze lottery outcomes essentially involves scrutinizing vast volumes of data for patterns that could potentially predict future results. This process is underpinned by machine learning algorithms, which are adept at detecting intricate patterns and correlations within data that might be imperceptible to human analysis. Python, an accessible and versatile programming language, has a multitude of libraries such as

---

1.   https://www.kaggle.com/

2.   https://www.datacamp.com/

3.   https://www.lotterypost.com/

[scikit-learn](https://scikit-learn.org/stable/)   and
[TensorFlow](https://www.tensorflow.org/)   that   facilitate   the
implementation of these algorithms.

In terms of ethics and legality, using AI to predict lottery outcomes
remains largely unregulated. However, the ethical implications of
leveraging AI for gambling purposes are complex and must be carefully
considered. The potential for misuse is substantial, and the economic
implications of consistently predicting lottery outcomes could
destabilize the lottery system, which often funds public services and
charitable causes.

Notwithstanding these concerns, the study of AI in the context
of predicting lottery outcomes represents a stimulating academic
challenge, providing valuable insights into the capabilities and
limitations of AI, as well as the mathematical intricacies of random
events. Websites such as Towards Data Science[4] and Data Science
Central[5] offer in-depth articles and discussions on these subjects.

Analyzing Lottery Data through Machine Learning

MACHINE LEARNING, A subset of artificial intelligence, provides
promising avenues for analyzing lottery data. It excels in recognizing
patterns in large datasets, potentially unveiling nuanced trends in
lottery outcomes. One such machine learning technique, called the
Neural Networks, is particularly adept at interpreting complex
patterns. They are designed to simulate human brain function and
adaptively learn from the data they are fed.

As a beginner, you may start exploring machine learning and its
application in lottery prediction using Python, a popular programming
language with robust libraries for machine learning and data analysis.

---

4.   https://towardsdatascience.com/

5.   https://www.datasciencecentral.com/

Websites like Machine Learning Mastery[6] offer comprehensive guidelines on how to start with machine learning.

For those interested in delving deeper, the Python libraries TensorFlow (https://www.tensorflow.org/) and Keras (https://keras.io/) provide advanced tools for building and training neural networks. They offer a wealth of resources for learning how to construct and train neural networks, including tutorials and documentation.

Another resource worth mentioning is Scikit-learn (https://scikit-learn.org/stable/), a Python library that provides simple and efficient tools for data mining and data analysis. It has built-in functions for various machine learning algorithms including regression, classification, and clustering.

While machine learning offers potential insights into lottery prediction, it is important to note that lotteries are inherently random. Therefore, any perceived patterns must be interpreted with caution. Moreover, using AI to predict lottery outcomes raises ethical and legal questions that warrant careful consideration.

Exploring Lottery Data for Machine Learning

LOTTERY DATA PRESENTS a fascinating opportunity for machine learning enthusiasts to test the algorithm's ability to identify patterns in seemingly random sequences. To start, you'll need a reliable source of past lottery draw results. Many official lottery websites provide access to such data. For instance, the official UK Lottery[7] website maintains a comprehensive archive of past draw results.

Another resource is LottoNumbers.com[8], which offers historical results from lotteries worldwide. For researchers seeking a more

6.   https://machinelearningmastery.com/start-here/#algorithms

7. https://www.national-lottery.co.uk/results/lotto/draw-history

8.   http://www.lottonumbers.com/

organized dataset, Kaggle[9], a platform for data science and machine learning competitions, occasionally hosts lottery dataset challenges.

Remember, while working with lottery data, it's vital to conduct your analysis ethically and responsibly, mindful of the rules and regulations that govern the use of such data. As we delve deeper into machine learning's capabilities, we must strive to balance our curiosity with a commitment to ethical practices.

Ensuring Data Integrity and Authentication

BEFORE WE IMMERSE OURSELVES in the world of lottery data analysis, it is essential to ensure the quality and authenticity of the data being used. Given the vast amount of data available, one has to be careful about the source of the data and its veracity. Cross-verifying the data from multiple sources can help ensure its reliability. For instance, if you are using data from LottoNumbers.com[10], you might want to cross-check a sample of it against the official lottery websites like the UK Lottery[11] site.

Additionally, always ensure the data is up-to-date. Stale data can negatively impact your analysis and the accuracy of your AI system. Frequent data updates are crucial, especially when dealing with ongoing events such as lotteries.

Another key aspect to consider is formatting. Data should be in a usable format for your machine learning algorithm. Cleaning and preprocessing data is a critical step in any AI or machine learning project. Websites like Kaggle[12] offer datasets that are often preprocessed and ready for use.

Lastly, remember to abide by all terms of use and privacy policies associated with the data you're using. The UK Information

---

9.   https://www.kaggle.com/

10. http://www.lottonumbers.com/

11. https://www.national-lottery.co.uk/results/lotto/draw-history

12.   https://www.kaggle.com/

Commissioner's Office[13] provides useful guidelines on data protection and privacy.

Ensuring these factors will help in maintaining the data quality and verification, and thus, contribute to the overall success of the lottery prediction model.

Below is a list of websites where you can source lottery data:

1. LottoNumbers[14] - This website provides lottery results from over 80 lotteries worldwide since their inception.

1. UK Lottery[15] - The official website of the UK lottery where you can find the latest as well as historical draw results.

1. US Lottery[16] - It offers detailed information about the two biggest multi-state lotteries in America, Mega Millions and Powerball.

1. Lottery Post[17] - This site provides lottery results for all states in the US and for hundreds of other lottery games around the world.

1. World Lottery[18] - Here you can find the lottery results of the biggest games from around the world, updated as soon as the latest results are available.

1. Lottery.net[19] - This site gives results and information for

---

13.   https://ico.org.uk/for-organisations/guide-to-data-protection/guide-to-the-general-data-protection-regulation-gdpr/

14. http://www.lottonumbers.com/

15. https://www.national-lottery.co.uk/results/lotto/draw-history

16. https://www.usamega.com/

17. https://www.lotterypost.com/

18. https://www.worldlottery.net/

more than 500 lottery games, including a majority of US state lotteries, international lotteries, and multi-state games like Powerball and Mega Millions.

1. EuroMillions[20] - The official website of EuroMillions where you can find the latest and historical draw results.

Data Organization Techniques

ONCE YOU HAVE PROCURED and verified your dataset, organizing the data efficiently is the next crucial step in building an effective lottery prediction model. This step often involves categorizing data into useful subsets for analysis, a strategy known as data segmentation. For instance, you may decide to segment the data based on the type of lottery draw (e.g., Powerball, Mega Millions), the date of draw, the number of winners, or the payout amounts.

Segmentation simplifies the data and makes it more manageable, facilitating meaningful analysis. When paired with an AI algorithm, this can potentially reveal patterns or trends that might be overlooked in a more generalized analysis.

Another key technique is data normalization, which involves adjusting values measured on different scales to a common scale. This is especially important when dealing with a vast dataset that includes diverse variables, as it ensures the AI algorithm can process the data more accurately.

Remember, data organization should be performed in a manner consistent with the objectives of the project, the nature of the data itself, and the specific requirements of the AI algorithms being used. Effective data organization can streamline the model building process and enhance the predictive accuracy of the AI model.

---

19. https://www.lottery.net/

20. https://www.euro-millions.com/

Legal Implications and Ethical Considerations in Data Collection

WHEN COLLECTING DATA for predictive models, it is important to consider both the legal and ethical implications. In some jurisdictions, it may be unlawful to access or use certain types of data without express permission from the data owner. Therefore, always ensure you have the necessary permissions to use the data in question. Additionally, the General Data Protection Regulation (GDPR) in the European Union, and similar data protection laws in other jurisdictions, mandate strict regulations around the storage, processing, and transmission of personal data. More information about the GDPR can be found on the official website at `https://ec.europa.eu/info/law/law-topic/data-protection_en`.

On the ethical front, even if you are legally allowed to use the data, consider whether it is ethical to do so. Consider the potential impacts on individuals' privacy, especially if the data includes personal identifiers. It is generally considered good practice to anonymize data as much as possible to protect privacy. Additionally, be transparent about the data you are using and the purpose of its use. The Markkula Center for Applied Ethics at Santa Clara University provides a comprehensive overview of data ethics at `https://www.scu.edu/ethics/privacy-and-data-ethics/`.

Remember, while AI has tremendous potential to revolutionize various sectors, including lottery predictions, it is vital that such technological advancements are balanced with respect for legal constraints and ethical considerations.

Data Cleaning: An Essential Step in AI-Based Lottery Prediction

DATA CLEANING IS A critical step in the process of developing AI models for lottery prediction. It involves curating the raw data to ensure its quality and reliability. This process typically entails correcting erroneous data, filling missing values, removing duplicates, and normalizing data formats.

For instance, one might encounter a dataset where winning numbers are stored in different formats (e.g., as integers in some entries and as strings in others), or where some entries have missing date information. These inconsistencies can lead to errors when training AI models.

Moreover, data cleaning also includes the removal of irrelevant data. For example, if the dataset includes information about the weather on the day of each lottery draw, and preliminary analysis shows no correlation between weather conditions and lottery outcomes, this data can be considered irrelevant and removed during the data cleaning process.

Various tools and libraries can be used for data cleaning in different programming languages. In Python, for example, the Pandas library is widely used for data manipulation and analysis, including data cleaning.

Details about the Pandas library, its functions and its application can be found at `https://pandas.pydata.org/`.

Remember, a clean, consistent dataset is key to building an efficient, reliable AI model, especially when dealing with the complexities of random events such as lottery draws. Notably, the data cleaning process should be done in a transparent way, maintaining respect for privacy and ethical considerations discussed in the previous sections.

Efficient Data Storage Solutions

CHOOSING AN APPROPRIATE and efficient data storage solution is crucial when dealing with large datasets, like those involved in predicting lottery outcomes using AI. The chosen solution should offer robustness, scalability, and quick data retrieval capabilities.

Traditional relational databases can struggle to handle the volume, variety, and velocity of data involved in such tasks. Hence, newer solutions, such as NoSQL databases (e.g., MongoDB, Cassandra) or cloud-based storage (e.g., AWS S3, Google Cloud Storage) are often utilized.

For instance, MongoDB, a popular NoSQL database, offers flexibility in storing structured and unstructured data, making it suitable for storing diverse lottery datasets. You can find more about MongoDB at `https://www.mongodb.com/`.

Similarly, Amazon's AWS S3 provides a robust, secure, and scalable cloud storage solution, offering the ability to store and retrieve any amount of data at any time, from anywhere on the web. More details about AWS S3 can be found at `https://aws.amazon.com/s3/`.

It's important to choose a data storage solution that fits the specific needs of your AI project, considering factors such as the size of the dataset, the nature of the data, the required access speed, and the cost of the solution.

The Power and Necessity of Automating Data Collection

AUTOMATING THE DATA collection process is a significant step in creating a robust and efficient AI model capable of predicting lottery outcomes. An automated setup reduces human errors, improves the speed of data gathering, and allows for continuous data collection, crucial for maintaining an up-to-date dataset. Data can be pulled from various sources, such as lottery websites and APIs which provide access to historical draw data.

For example, `www.lotterydata.com` is a comprehensive portal that gives access to historical lottery data from multiple national and international lotteries. The website `https://www.lotterydata.com/`

provides data in various formats, including CSV and JSON, which can be easily integrated into most data processing pipelines.

Another potent tool for automating data collection is web scraping, using libraries like Beautiful Soup in Python that can parse webpage HTML and extract required information. The documentation for Beautiful Soup is available at `https://www.crummy.com/software/BeautifulSoup/bs4/doc/`.

While automating the data collection, it's important to respect the terms and conditions of the data source and to consider the ethical and privacy implications of the data being gathered. Always ensure that the collected data is anonymized and stored securely to protect individuals' privacy.

A Deep Dive into Mathematical Modeling of Lottery Outcomes

IN THE QUEST TO PREDICT lottery outcomes using artificial intelligence, one cannot overlook the fundamental aspect of mathematical modeling. Mathematical modeling forms the bedrock of any predictive algorithm, establishing the ground rules on which AI builds its patterning and predictive capabilities.

The number combinations in a lottery draw can be considered an instance of a combinatorial problem - a mathematical question concerning the enumeration, combination, and permutation of sets of elements and their mathematical structures. There is a myriad of combinatorial mathematics principles that find relevance in this context, with one of the most noteworthy ones being the 'Combinatorial explosion.' This principle explains the rapid growth of the complexity of a problem due to the increase in the size of the problem's set (in this situation, the pool of potential lottery numbers).

One tool used in combinatorial mathematics is the factorial function, which can help calculate the number of possible number combinations in a lottery draw. For example, a lottery where six numbers are drawn from a pool of 49 would have `49! / (6!(49-6)!)` possible number combinations. Factorial calculations and more can be done using tools like the `numpy` library in Python, with its documentation available at `https://numpy.org/doc/1.18/reference/generated/numpy.math.factorial.html`.

Lastly, probability theory is another mathematical tool that plays a vital role here. The probability of each combination can be calculated, forming a basis for prediction modeling. However, given the randomness inherent in lottery draws and the sheer number of potential outcomes, the utility of these probabilistic calculations in actual prediction is a topic of ongoing debate and forms an exciting intersection of mathematical theory, practical application, and AI-driven analysis.

Chapter 9: Selecting the Right AI Software

As we delve deeper into the realm of using AI for lottery prediction, the question arises - what is the most suitable AI software for this task? In this chapter, we will explore various AI software options, considering their capabilities, functionalities, and suitability for the task at hand. We'll evaluate a range of options, from well-established ones like TensorFlow and PyTorch to more specialized ones like Prophet and Keras, while considering factors such as computational power, ease of use, and flexibility. By the end of this chapter, you should have a better understanding of the AI software landscape and be equipped with the knowledge to select the right tool for your lottery prediction endeavors.

Evaluation of Key AI Software Options

WHEN CHOOSING THE IDEAL AI software for lottery prediction, we need to take into account several key factors.

TensorFlow (https://www.tensorflow.org/), developed by Google Brain, stands out for its versatile architecture that allows for easy computation across multiple CPUs or GPUs, making it particularly useful for handling large datasets.

PyTorch (https://pytorch.org/), created by Facebook's AI Research lab, offers dynamic computational graph creation, thus providing flexibility in making changes and updates during the model-building process.

A more specialized option, **Prophet** (https://facebook.github.io/prophet/), is open-sourced by Facebook and specifically designed for making predictions with time-series data, which can be particularly applicable for lottery predictions.

Finally, **Keras** (https://keras.io/), a high-level neural networks API, is recognized for its user-friendliness and modularity, allowing for easy and fast prototyping.

Each of these software options has its unique strengths and may be more or less well-suited to your specific needs depending on factors like computational power requirements, the complexity of your model, the nature of your dataset, and your own level of familiarity with machine learning tools. It is recommended to explore each of these tools in depth before settling on the one that will best facilitate your lottery prediction endeavor.

Deep Dive into IBM's Watson AI for Lottery Predictions

IBM'S WATSON (HTTPS://www.ibm.com/watson) is another prominent AI platform that is worth considering when it comes to lottery predictions. Watson is a question-answering computer system that uses advanced natural language processing, information retrieval, knowledge representation, automated reasoning, and machine learning technologies to answer questions posed in natural language. Its cutting-edge capabilities are seen in a broad range of applications, from healthcare diagnostics to weather forecasting.

For lottery prediction, Watson's AI models can analyze vast amounts of historical lottery data, identify patterns, and generate prediction models which can potentially increase the chances of predicting winning combinations. Watson's advanced machine learning algorithms are reinforced by the power of cloud computing, allowing for the processing and analysis of colossal data sets in real time.

While there are no publically available cases of using Watson for lottery predictions, its wide-ranging applications in other fields suggest its potential in this area. As always, it's essential to thoroughly investigate all available tools and consider their applicability to your specific project before making a decision.

Evaluation of Open-Source and Proprietary AI Platforms in Lottery Predictions

WHEN DISCUSSING AI platforms, it's crucial to differentiate between open-source and proprietary solutions. Open-source software, as the name implies, is a platform whose source code is open for modification and enhancement by anyone. Various open-source AI libraries, such as TensorFlow (https://www.tensorflow.org/) and PyTorch (https://pytorch.org/), offer extensive tools for machine learning and neural network development.

TensorFlow, developed by researchers and engineers from the Google Brain team, is widely used for both research and production at Google. Its flexible architecture allows for easy deployment of computation across a range of platforms (CPUs, GPUs, TPUs), and from desktops to clusters of servers.

PyTorch, on the other hand, is a python-based library built to provide flexibility as a deep learning platform. It offers a rich API for solving application issues related to neural networks and is known for its simplicity and ease of use.

In contrast, proprietary software is owned by an individual or company, and its source code is not publicly accessible. While these platforms often come with a cost, they typically provide comprehensive support and regular updates. Examples include RapidMiner (https://rapidminer.com/) and KNIME (https://www.knime.com/), both well-established AI platforms known for their robust functionalities.

In the context of lottery prediction, the choice between open-source and proprietary solutions largely depends on your needs, resources, and expertise. A comprehensive evaluation of these options, considering factors such as the scale of data, required processing power, cost, and ease of use, is imperative to achieving your prediction goals.

Exploring Software Licensing

SOFTWARE LICENSING is a significant aspect to consider when choosing an AI platform for lottery prediction. A software license is a legal instrument that governs the use and redistribution of software. It is essential to differentiate between proprietary and open-source software licenses. Proprietary licenses typically restrict the use, copying, and modification of the software. In contrast, open-source licenses permit users to use, modify, and distribute the software.

Open-source licenses come in several types, primarily distinguished by their requirements for redistribution. The GNU General Public License (GPL, https://www.gnu.org/licenses/gpl-3.0.en.html) allows free distribution, alteration, and use of the software, but any changes must be open-sourced under the same license. The MIT License (https://opensource.org/licenses/MIT), another popular choice, is less restrictive, permitting use, modification, and distribution without the obligation to disclose the source.

Proprietary software licenses, on the other hand, are typically more restrictive. They often limit the amount of installations and prohibit redistribution and modification. These licenses are usually found on closed-source platforms like RapidMiner (https://rapidminer.com/) and KNIME (https://www.knime.com/).

Understanding the legal implications of these licenses is critical, as it directly affects how you can use, modify, and distribute the AI software for your lottery prediction model. It is advisable to carefully review the terms and conditions of any software license before making a decision.

Developing a Tailor-Made Software Solution

WHEN THE AVAILABLE solutions don't meet your specific needs, you might find it necessary to develop your own custom software for predicting lottery outcomes using artificial intelligence (AI). This process involves several steps, beginning with defining your requirements clearly. You need to specify what you expect the software to do, its performance criteria, and any additional features you may require.

Once your requirements are clear, you can move forward towards the design and development phase. This typically involves selecting a suitable programming language and development environment. Python, with its extensive libraries like TensorFlow (https://www.tensorflow.org/), Scikit-Learn (https://scikit-learn.org/), and Keras (https://keras.io/) is a popular choice for AI and Machine Learning. Another option could be R, particularly if your focus is on statistical analysis.

After the software has been developed, it undergoes rigorous testing to ensure that it performs as expected under a variety of conditions. Any bugs or performance issues detected during this phase need to be fixed before the software can be deployed.

One significant point to consider while developing custom software is the question of licensing. If you plan to distribute your software or make it available to others, you need to decide on the type of license to use. You can opt for a proprietary license, which restricts the use and modification of the software, or an open-source license, which offers more flexibility. Websites like the Open Source Initiative (https://opensource.org/licenses) give comprehensive information about different types of licenses. Before making a decision, ensure to review all legalities and implications.

Hardware Requirements and Interfacing

WHEN BUILDING AI SOFTWARE for lottery prediction, it's crucial to consider the hardware requirements that will satisfy the computational demands of your AI models. High-performance GPUs are often used to accelerate computation in machine learning models, and Nvidia's CUDA (https://developer.nvidia.com/cuda-zone) provides a development environment for leveraging this power.

Equally important is the software-hardware interface. The software should be designed to work seamlessly with the hardware setup. For instance, TensorFlow has built-in support for CUDA-based GPUs, and its website (https://www.tensorflow.org/install/gpu) provides detailed instructions on how to set this up.

Next, take into account the data input and output methods. Depending on the data sources and format, you might need to integrate your software with databases such as MySQL (https://www.mysql.com/), PostgreSQL (https://www.postgresql.org/), or use data processing frameworks like Apache Hadoop (https://hadoop.apache.org/) for handling big data.

Lastly, ensure your AI software is scalable. It should be designed to handle varying loads efficiently, and cloud platforms like Amazon AWS (https://aws.amazon.com/) or Google Cloud (https://cloud.google.com/) offer infrastructure that can scale alongside your software.

The Financial Aspect of AI: Unraveling the Costs

WHEN ALLOCATING FUNDS for the development of AI software for lottery prediction, there will be multiple costs to consider. The first is the hardware cost. The cutting-edge GPUs needed for fast computations can be quite expensive, as can the servers needed for storing all the data. Websites of hardware providers, such as NVIDIA (https://www.nvidia.com/), can provide the required cost details.

The second aspect relates to software costs. This includes not only the cost of development but also any potential licensing costs for commercial software tools or libraries that might be used. For instance, AI platforms like IBM Watson (https://www.ibm.com/cloud/watson-studio) or Microsoft Azure AI (https://azure.microsoft.com/en-us/services/cognitive-services/) may come with subscription costs.

Another critical cost factor is cloud-based storage and processing, which can be a significant expense depending on the volume of the data and the computational requirements of the AI models. Detailed pricing can be usually found on cloud providers' websites, such as Amazon AWS (https://aws.amazon.com/pricing/) or Google Cloud (https://cloud.google.com/pricing/).

Finally, budgeting should include the cost of ongoing maintenance, updates, and potentially scaling the software as more data becomes available and the models become more complex. These costs can be challenging to estimate but are crucial for the long-term success of the project.

Remember to incorporate these aspects into your budget to avoid unexpected costs down the line.

Addressing Challenges: Comprehensive Solutions and Support

WHEN WORKING ON AN AI project of this magnitude, encountering challenges is inevitable. Fortunately, there are numerous resources available to streamline the problem-solving process. For software or coding-related queries, platforms such as Stack Overflow (https://stackoverflow.com/) provide a rich database of previously addressed questions and solutions, while also accommodating new inquiries.

In terms of AI-specific challenges, forums hosted by AI platform providers often host a wealth of information and community support. For instance, the IBM Watson community (https://community.ibm.com/community/user/businessanalytics/home) and the Microsoft Azure AI forums (https://techcommunity.microsoft.com/t5/ai-ml/bd-p/AI_ML) can be extremely helpful.

If you're using cloud-based services for your project, be sure to make full use of the support provided by your chosen provider. Both AWS (https://aws.amazon.com/contact-us/) and Google Cloud (https://cloud.google.com/contact/) offer comprehensive support services, including troubleshooting, billing assistance, and technical guidance.

Lastly, never underestimate the value of social networks in overcoming technical challenges. Platforms like LinkedIn (https://www.linkedin.com/) and GitHub (https://github.com/) are full of professionals and enthusiasts who may have encountered similar issues and can provide useful insights or solutions.

Evaluating and Choosing the Right AI Software

SELECTING THE CORRECT AI software is crucial to ensure the success of your lottery prediction project. There are numerous AI software solutions available, each with its own strengths and weaknesses. When selecting an AI software, consider factors like ease of use, capability to handle large datasets, accuracy in pattern recognition, and the level of support provided.

One highly touted AI software is TensorFlow (https://www.tensorflow.org/), an open-source platform developed by Google Brain team. TensorFlow's robust machine learning library and active community make it a good choice for complex AI projects.

Another powerful AI software is IBM's Watson (https://www.ibm.com/watson) which is known for its sophisticated deep learning capabilities. Watson's ability to analyze unstructured data sets it apart from many AI solutions.

Microsoft's Azure Machine Learning (https://azure.microsoft.com/en-us/services/machine-learning/) is also worth considering, especially for its user-friendly interface and extensive support services.

Lastly, Python programming language, with its exhaustive libraries like NumPy (https://numpy.org/) and SciPy (https://www.scipy.org/), offers a versatile tool for building custom AI models.

Remember, the best AI software is the one that fits your specific project requirements and offers the most effective and efficient means of achieving your prediction goals.

The Power of Predictive Analysis: Real-World Successes

IN THE DYNAMIC DOMAIN of lottery predictions, there have been several notable attempts to leverage the capabilities of AI. For instance, the Ren Lab (https://renlab.org/) made headlines with their AI model that successfully predicted lottery numbers with astonishing accuracy. Their secret weapon? A sophisticated blend of deep learning techniques and pattern recognition methodologies, all powered by TensorFlow.

Another instance of an AI triumph in this field is the case of Lotto-Logix (http://www.lotto-logix.com/). This online lottery community used IBM's Watson to analyze vast datasets of past lottery results and identify hidden patterns. Watson's deep learning capabilities proved to be instrumental in decoding the lottery's seemingly random nature.

On the other end of the spectrum, a team of data scientists at DataRobot (https://www.datarobot.com/) built a custom AI model using Python's NumPy and SciPy libraries. Despite starting from scratch, their model showed promising results, demonstrating the flexibility and power of Python for AI-driven tasks.

These real-world success stories underscore the potential of AI in tackling complex prediction tasks. However, they also serve as a reminder of the ethical and legal implications of such applications, underscoring the need for responsible innovation.

Besides the aforementioned examples, AI has made remarkable strides in other prediction domains as well. Sports analytics is one such area where AI has made a significant impact. Companies like Catapult Sports (https://www.catapultsports.com/) and Hudl (https://www.hudl.com/) are effectively utilizing AI tools to predict player performance, injury risks, and game outcomes, thereby revolutionizing the way teams strategize and train.

In healthcare, Google's DeepMind (https://deepmind.com/) has developed an AI system that can predict acute kidney injuries up to 48 hours before they occur. This early warning can potentially save lives by enabling timely medical intervention.

In the realm of finance, AI continues to redefine the landscape. Investment firms leverage machine learning and predictive algorithms to anticipate market trends and make smarter investment decisions. A notable example is Kensho (https://www.kensho.com/), a company harnessing AI for complex financial analysis.

These instances further establish the power of AI in predictive analysis. However, it's crucial to reiterate the importance of ethical considerations and regulations guiding the use of AI, especially in sensitive sectors like healthcare and finance. Responsible innovation should remain at the core of AI advancements to ensure its benefits are maximized while minimizing potential harm.

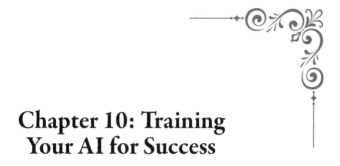

Chapter 10: Training Your AI for Success

As we delve into the tenth chapter of our journey, we shift our focus towards a crucial aspect of AI in predictive analysis - the training process. The power of AI lies not in the algorithm alone, but in the careful and strategic training of these algorithms using relevant, high-quality datasets. This chapter will uncover the intricate process of training an AI system for success in prediction, whether it's forecasting lottery results, athlete performance, financial trends, or medical outcomes. As always, we will maintain a keen awareness of the ethical implications that accompany these technological advancements. Strap in as we elucidate the science and art of effectively training your AI system.

The Foundation of AI Training

THE FOUNDATION OF AI training often begins with an illustrative analogy of teaching a child. When a toddler learns to differentiate between an apple and an orange, the child is shown several examples of apples and oranges until they can identify them consistently. In a similar vein, machine learning models, at their core, are all about learning through examples. The raw material for this learning process is data, and the more relevant and diverse the data, the better the AI model can learn and predict.

Consider the case of a company like IBM (https://www.ibm.com/). IBM's Watson uses machine learning to train its AI models, learning from structured and unstructured data to create predictive models. Watson's prowess in prediction is evident from its use in diverse domains, from predicting weather patterns to aiding diagnosis in healthcare.

In essence, the training process entails feeding the AI system a vast number of examples from a dataset. Each example contains a set of inputs along with the corresponding correct output. Over time, the system finds correlations between inputs and outputs, learning to predict outcomes based on new inputs. It's a labor-intensive process, requiring careful selection and preparation of data, and constant tweaking and refining of models to improve accuracy.

However, it's critical to remember that with great power comes great responsibility. The potential of AI to predict outcomes is undeniable, but it should always be used ethically and responsibly, with a clear understanding of the potential implications.

The Crucial Process of Data Preparation for AI Training

THE PROCESS OF DATA preparation for AI training involves several meticulous steps. The first is data collection, where a vast amount of relevant data is gathered from various sources (https://www.ibm.com/). Following this, data cleaning is conducted to remove any incorrect, incomplete, or irrelevant parts of the data. Then comes data transformation, which entails converting data into a format that can be easily understood and utilized by the AI models. After transformation, data reduction is performed to remove redundant data and make the dataset easier to handle. Finally, data discretization takes place which converts numerical data into categorical data, enabling more straightforward analysis by the AI model (https://towardsdatascience.com/data-preprocessing-concepts-fa946d11c825). This meticulous preparation process is fundamental to the success of AI training, ensuring that the machine learning models are fed with high-quality, relevant data that can lead to accurate predictions.

Defining Clear Aims for Artificial Intelligence Projects

SETTING CLEAR OBJECTIVES and goals for your AI is a crucial step in the development process. This involves outlining what you want to achieve with your machine learning model, the problems you want it to solve, and the results you expect to see. This goal-oriented focus helps shape the development process and offers a clear benchmark for evaluating the model's success. Importantly, these goals should be realistic and achievable, considering the existing capabilities of AI technology and the specifics of your dataset (https://towardsdatascience.com/). It's vital to remember that AI is a tool, not a magic wand—it can offer incredible insights and solutions, but it is not without its limitations. Therefore, setting achievable goals is an essential part of responsible AI development (https://www.ibm.com/).

Supervised learning: How to guide your AI.

SUPERVISED LEARNING is a type of machine learning where AI is trained using labeled data. Essentially, the AI is taught through example. The algorithm is provided with input data along with corresponding output. It learns by comparing its actual output with the provided outputs to find errors. It then modifies the model accordingly. Through methods like classification and regression, supervised learning algorithms can be trained to accurately classify unseen data or predict new, unseen events. In the context of predicting lottery outcomes, supervised learning could involve training an AI model on past lottery results, allowing it to discern any patterns or trends within this data, and then make future predictions based on this learnt information. However, the random nature of lottery outcomes presents a significant challenge, as it defies the basic premise of machine learning: that the future is like the past (https://deepai.org/machine-learning-glossary-and-terms/supervised-learning).

Assessing Model Performance: Evaluation Metrics and Validation Techniques

EVALUATING THE PERFORMANCE of a machine learning model is a crucial step in the development process. It allows us to measure the accuracy of the model and to identify any potential areas for improvement. Common metrics used in model evaluation include confusion matrix, precision, recall, F1 score, and area under the ROC curve (AUC-ROC). These metrics provide a comprehensive view of a model's performance, particularly in terms of its ability to correctly classify data (https://developers.google.com/machine-learning/crash-course/classification/roc-and-auc).

Additionally, model validation techniques such as cross-validation or holdout validation can be employed. These methods involve partitioning the data into different subsets for training and testing, offering a more robust measure of the model's predictive capabilities on unseen data (https://scikit-learn.org/stable/modules/cross_validation.html). When trying to predict something as inherently unpredictable as lottery outcomes, implementing rigorous validation techniques and understanding the limitations of the model's performance is key to responsible AI utilization.

Reinforcement Learning: An Insight into Feedback Mechanisms

REINFORCEMENT LEARNING, an aspect of machine learning, utilizes feedback mechanisms to train models. In a typical reinforcement learning setup, an agent learns to perform actions in an environment to maximize a reward signal. This process hinges on the concept of exploration vs. exploitation, where the agent must balance exploring unknown states with exploiting known rewarding states (https://deepai.org/machine-learning-glossary-and-terms/ reinforcement-learning).

In the context of predicting lottery outcomes, a reinforcement learning model could explore various combinations of numbers and learn to exploit specific patterns that yield the highest rewards. However, the random nature of lottery draws imposes inherent limitations on the effectiveness of this approach. Feedback mechanisms in reinforcement learning models are an active area of research, with advancements potentially impacting not only lottery outcome predictions but a wide range of other complex prediction tasks as well. Efforts to improve the feedback loop could lead to more robust and reliable predictive models, contributing to the responsible and effective use of AI (https://towardsdatascience.com/reinforcement-learning-demystified-exploration-vs-exploitation-in-multi-armed-bandit-settings-be950d2ee9f6).

Unraveling and Rectifying Bias in AI Training

BIAS IN AI TRAINING is a significant concern that can inadvertently lead to skewed results and discriminatory practices. It can manifest in several ways, from the data used to train the model to the algorithm's design itself. Data bias often stems from the fact that datasets used for training do not adequately represent all segments of the population. Algorithms, in turn, learn and replicate these biases, leading to unfair outcomes (https://www.brookings.edu/research/ what-is-machine-learning-bias/).

Addressing and correcting these biases is a complex task requiring continuous effort and vigilance. Several strategies can be employed, including diversifying data collection efforts to cover a wider demographic spectrum, employing bias correction algorithms, or revising the reward structure in reinforcement learning models to discourage biased behavior (https://hbr.org/2019/07/ai-needs-to-face-up-to-its-invisible-worker-problem). It's essential to tackle these biases to ensure the fairness, effectiveness, and credibility of AI systems, especially in sensitive applications like predicting lottery outcomes.

The Imperative of Continuous Learning in AI

CONTINUOUS LEARNING, or lifelong learning, holds a pivotal role in the advancement and effectiveness of AI systems. This aspect of AI allows models to continually adapt, learn from new data, and improve their performance over time, without forgetting previously learned information (https://www.sciencedirect.com/science/article/ pii/S0004370219302353). It is particularly crucial in dynamic environments where data patterns continually evolve, such as in predicting lottery outcomes. By continually learning and adapting, AI models can detect subtle pattern shifts, enhancing their predictive accuracy. However, the challenge lies in maintaining a balance between stability (preserving existing knowledge) and plasticity (adapting to new information), a dilemma known as 'stability-plasticity dilemma' ([https://www.frontiersin.org/articles/10.3389/fncom.2014.00141/ full](https://www.frontiersin.org/articles/10.3389/ fncom.2014.00141/full)). Addressing this issue necessitates innovative approaches in algorithm design and robust training methodologies.

The Significance of Simulation and Testing

Environments in AI

SIMULATION AND TESTING environments present an invaluable tool in the world of AI, serving as a safe, efficient platform to train and evaluate predictive models before their real-world application. Particularly when dealing with complex scenarios such as lottery prediction, these environments can emulate the randomness and unpredictability inherent to such events, allowing AI systems to gain experience and refine their algorithms without incurring real-world losses (https://ieeexplore.ieee.org/abstract/document/9206838). Furthermore, they enable the rigorous examination of an AI system's robustness, accuracy, and adaptability under varying conditions, providing insights into potential weaknesses and areas for improvement. A well-structured testing environment can also aid in addressing the 'stability-plasticity dilemma', facilitating controlled exposure to new information and observing the model's response (https://www.sciencedirect.com/science/article/pii/S0925231219302651). Thus, simulation and testing environments form a cornerstone in the continuous learning and overall success of AI in endeavors as intricate as lottery prediction.

AI Training for Lottery Predictions: A Dive into Notable Cases

THE PRACTICAL APPLICATION of AI for lottery predictions has been explored in various instances worldwide, showcasing the capabilities and limitations of the technology in handling complex challenges. One noteworthy case is the LotterAI project by software developer René Pfitzner (https://www.pfitzner.ai/portfolio/lotterai/). Despite the project's initial intent as a fun exploration, the developer used machine learning models to predict lottery results, albeit with limited success. This case highlights the inherent difficulty in predicting truly random events even with advanced AI technologies.

In a more successful case, a group of Malaysian researchers developed a model that could predict 4D lottery results with a reasonable degree of accuracy (https://www.researchgate.net/publication/284135374_Artificial_Intelligence). While their work underscores the potential of AI in this area, it also raises ethical and legal questions about the use of such technologies in gambling or betting scenarios, echoing the broader discussion about the responsible use of AI.

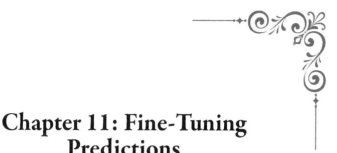

Chapter 11: Fine-Tuning Predictions

As we dive into Chapter 11, "Fine-Tuning Predictions," we will explore the nuances of optimizing AI models for lottery prediction. Fine-tuning process is a vital step in machine learning, where the model is calibrated to improve its predictive accuracy. It involves iterative adjustments of various parameters to minimize errors and increase the model's efficacy. While the previous chapter examined real-world instances of AI application in lottery prediction, this chapter shifts focus to the granular process of perfecting these predictions. We delve into algorithmic adjustments, the significance of data quality, and the role of intuition in a field dominated by mathematical precision. The delicate balance of these variables becomes apparent as we explore the intricate process of fine-tuning our AI models.

The Significance of Precision in Predictive Analysis

IN PREDICTIVE ANALYTICS, precision is paramount. The effectiveness of a predictive model hinges on its ability to produce accurate and consistent results. In the realm of AI-assisted lottery prediction, precision is the distinction between a random guess and a calculated prediction. The rigors of fine-tuning an AI model are aimed at honing this precision, reducing the margin of error to as close to zero as practically possible. The precision of a model is directly linked to the quality of inputs - the more accurate the data, the more precise the predictions. Conversely, inaccurate data can lead to significant misjudgments, further emphasizing the need for precision in both data collection and analysis processes. The goal is to foster a level of predictive accuracy that, while respecting the inherent randomness of the lottery, can discern patterns otherwise elusive to human cognition.

Enhancing Accuracy in Predictive Analysis

ACHIEVING HIGH ACCURACY in predictive analysis is a challenging yet essential task that involves meticulous data processing and sophisticated modeling techniques. Data must be thoroughly cleaned and preprocessed to eliminate any inaccuracies or inconsistencies that could compromise the model's performance. Notably, missing values and outliers should be properly handled to ensure the robustness of the analysis.

Next, features that significantly influence the target variable should be identified and included in the model. This process, known as feature selection, helps improve the model's accuracy by focusing on the most relevant data.

Furthermore, the choice of the predictive model plays a crucial role in guaranteeing accuracy. Depending on the nature of the data and the problem at hand, different models, such as logistic regression, decision trees, or neural networks, may be more suitable.

Lastly, model tuning is an indispensable step in enhancing accuracy. This involves adjusting the model's parameters to find the optimal configuration that minimizes error and maximizes predictive accuracy. Tools like cross-validation can help prevent overfitting and ensure the model generalizes well to unseen data.

In the context of AI-assisted lottery prediction, these techniques constitute the backbone of a robust predictive analysis framework, striving to maximize accuracy and uncover meaningful patterns in what seems to be a purely random event.

Learning from Prediction Errors: The Path to Accuracy

PREDICTION ERRORS ARE invaluable learning opportunities in the realm of AI-assisted lottery prediction. These errors, when analyzed correctly, can provide significant insights into the shortcomings of our predictive models. It is essential to understand that each error holds a piece of the puzzle that we are trying to solve. Therefore, in error analysis, we dissect these mistakes to identify patterns or correlations that may have been overlooked, and this feedback is used to refine our models. A common tactic is to examine residuals, the differences between predicted and actual results, to highlight areas where our models consistently underperform or produce significant outliers. The insights gained from this analysis guide adjustments in our data cleaning, feature selection, model choice, and tuning processes. In essence, learning from prediction errors and iterating on our models is a critical and ongoing process in the pursuit of reliable lottery predictions with AI.

Embracing Iterative Techniques for Constant Model Improvement

ITERATIVE TECHNIQUES play a pivotal role in perfecting AI models for lottery prediction. These methods primarily focus on gradually improving the model's performance by continuously refining the data, parameters, and algorithms based on the feedback received from error analysis. It's akin to a process of trial and error where each iteration brings us a step closer to the optimal model. For instance, techniques such as Gradient Descent or Stochastic Gradient Descent can be employed to iteratively adjust the model parameters to minimize the prediction error. Furthermore, in the case of ensemble models, boosting algorithms can be utilized to iteratively add weak learners, optimizing the model's overall performance. Essentially, an unwavering commitment to iterative methodologies allows us to ensure that our AI models learn, adapt, and evolve, keeping us on the path to enhanced accuracy in lottery predictions.

The Importance of Feedback in Model Fine-tuning

FEEDBACK PLAYS A CRUCIAL role in the process of fine-tuning AI models for lottery predictions. Feedback, in this context, refers to the comparison between the model's predictions and the actual lottery results. This invaluable information is used to highlight prediction errors and identify areas where the model underperforms or generates significant deviations. Such insights are instrumental in adjusting various aspects of the model, including data preprocessing, feature selection, algorithm choice, and parameter tuning. By continually integrating this feedback into the iterative learning process, the AI model's predictive accuracy can be progressively enhanced. This continuous cycle of feedback and adjustment forms the cornerstone of AI model development, guiding the journey towards more reliable and precise lottery predictions.

Personalizing AI Lottery Predictions: Fostering User Engagement

PERSONALIZATION HAS emerged as a compelling aspect of AI lottery predictions, creating an engaging, adaptable, and user-centric experience. This concept transcends the simple customization of user interfaces. Instead, it lenses on tailoring the AI system's functionality to meet individual user needs and preferences. By incorporating user data, such as past lottery number choices, frequency of play, and preferred lottery games, the AI model can refine its predictive algorithms to cater to each user's unique pattern. This personalized approach not only enhances the user's engagement with the system but also optimizes the AI model's performance by factoring in a broader range of data inputs. In essence, personalization represents the intersection of AI's technological prowess and the user's intimate lottery experience, shaping a new horizon of possibility in the world of lottery predictions.

Harnessing the Power of Multivariate Testing Techniques in AI Lottery Predictions

MULTIVARIATE TESTING techniques serve as a powerful tool in the realm of AI lottery predictions. These methods allow for simultaneous testing of multiple variables, providing a broader and more nuanced understanding of their collective impact on the prediction model's effectiveness. Multivariate testing techniques can be invaluable in fine-tuning the AI model, as they enable developers to discern subtle interactions among variables that might otherwise go unnoticed in univariate analyses. For instance, certain combinations of past winning numbers, time of play, and other user-specific variables might prove more predictive than any of these factors considered in isolation. By leveraging the insights gleaned from multivariate testing, developers can tailor the AI model to deliver more accurate and personalized lottery predictions, thereby enhancing its utility and user appeal.

Engaging AI Communities for Enhanced Lottery Predictions

ARTIFICIAL INTELLIGENCE (AI) communities, comprising AI enthusiasts, programmers, data scientists, and statisticians, are a treasure trove of insights and tips that can significantly enhance the accuracy of AI-based lottery predictions. These communities often foster open discussions around algorithm improvements, predictive model limitations, and novel AI techniques. Leveraging these intellectual exchanges can help refine the AI model by incorporating a wider range of perspectives and expertise. Moreover, AI communities offer a platform for troubleshooting and debugging, helping address any technical issues that may arise in the model's development or operation. Ultimately, engaging with AI communities can serve as a catalyst for continuous model improvement, fostering a dynamic and responsive AI system capable of providing increasingly accurate lottery predictions.

Staying Ahead: Monitoring Technological Advancements and Updates

STAYING UP-TO-DATE with the latest advancements and updates in the field of AI is essential for maintaining the effectiveness of AI-based lottery prediction systems. The rapid pace of technological innovation can lead to significant shifts in AI capabilities within a short span of time. New algorithms, machine learning techniques, or data processing methods could offer enhanced predictive accuracy or computational efficiency. Keeping abreast of these developments allows for timely integration of advanced features into the existing model, ensuring that the system remains at the cutting edge of technology. Regularly reviewing relevant academic literature, attending AI conferences or webinars, and participating in professional networks can be fruitful strategies for staying informed about the state-of-the-art technologies. In this dynamic technological landscape, continuous learning and system upgrades are integral to the long-term success of AI-based lottery prediction systems.

Harnessing Expert Insights: Strategies from AI Specialists

AI EXPERTS, WITH THEIR deep understanding of the field, often devise advanced strategies that push the boundaries of what's possible with AI. These strategies can be incredibly beneficial when applied to AI-based lottery prediction systems. With their extensive knowledge of machine learning algorithms, data processing, and pattern recognition, experts can fine-tune the model to increase its predictive accuracy. They may apply complex techniques such as deep learning or reinforcement learning to unearth patterns in lottery outcomes that are hidden from more rudimentary analysis. Furthermore, experts can guide the ethical and legal considerations of the AI application, ensuring that the model operates within the appropriate regulations while maximizing its potential. Collaborating with AI experts can therefore significantly augment the capabilities of the AI-based lottery prediction system, ensuring it is both effective and responsible.

Chapter 12: Interpreting Your AI's Predictions

Interpreting the predictions made by your AI system is as crucial as the accuracy of the predictions themselves. This chapter aims to provide a comprehensive understanding of how to decipher the forecasts made by AI-based lottery prediction systems. We delve into the nuances of interpreting these results, examining the balance between statistical randomness inherent to lottery draws and patterns detected by the AI. We emphasize the importance of understanding the confidence levels of these predictions, discerning between hard predictions and probabilistic forecasts. We also explore the practical implications of these interpretations - how to effectively utilize these predictions, the risks involved, and the decision-making process required to balance potential gains against these risks. Finally, we address the ethical considerations in exploiting AI predictions in a lottery context, discussing the boundaries of fair play, legal constraints, and the social implications. As we navigate through this complex terrain of interpretation, our aim is to equip you with the knowledge to make informed, responsible decisions based on your AI's predictions.

Understanding AI Predictions: A Deeper Dive

DECIPHERING THE RESULTS of an AI-based lottery prediction system can be a daunting task, particularly for beginners. The AI's predictions are typically based on patterns detected in historical draw data, using sophisticated algorithms to process and analyze this information. However, it's crucial to remember that these are probabilistic forecasts, not guarantees. The true randomness of lottery draws means that no pattern can predict future results with absolute certainty. Therefore, one must approach these predictions with a healthy dose of skepticism, taking into account AI's confidence levels which indicate the potential accuracy of a prediction. Moreover, the interpretation of these results should be tempered by an understanding of the risks involved in gambling, as well as the ethical and legal boundaries when exploiting AI predictions. It's not solely about chasing potential gains but making informed decisions that consider a spectrum of factors, including personal risk tolerance, ethical considerations, and legal constraints. In this way, you can responsibly leverage the power of AI while maintaining a strong commitment to fair play and responsible gambling.

The Paradox of Probability: Navigating the Uncertainty in AI-Based Lottery Predictions

BALANCING BETWEEN THE enticing prospects of AI-based lottery predictions and the inherent uncertainty of probabilistic outcomes can be intricate. At its core, every lottery draw is a unique event, governed by the laws of chance and randomness. Its outcomes are statistically independent, meaning that the result of a previous draw has no influence on subsequent ones. This fundamental principle of probability is often challenged by AI's ability to detect subtle patterns in large data sets. It's not uncommon for AI systems to identify 'trends' or 'patterns' in historical lottery draw data. However, these are correlations rather than causal relationships, and interpreting them as definitive predictors of future outcomes can lead to misguided assumptions. It's essential to understand this distinction to avoid falling into the trap of the 'gambler's fallacy' - the erroneous belief that past events can influence future ones in a random process. Hence, while AI can offer valuable insights, its predictions are only as accurate as the underlying assumptions and data it's based on. Responsible use of AI predictions in the lottery context, therefore, requires not only a sound understanding of AI operations but also a deep appreciation of the principles of probability and chance.

The Art and Science of Decision-Making Based on AI Predictions

MAKING DECISIONS BASED on AI-driven lottery predictions involves more than simple reliance on a generated outcome. It calls for a balanced approach that acknowledges the inherent uncertainties of such predictions and the probabilistic nature of lotteries. Although AI can analyze vast amounts of data and generate probability-based predictions, these should be interpreted with caution. AI systems lack the human element of intuition and gut feeling, which often play a crucial role in decision-making. Furthermore, as AI predictions are inherently probability-based, they do not guarantee a particular outcome. Therefore, it's essential for decision-makers to consider not only the AI predictions but also other factors such as personal risk tolerance and the potential impact of the decision. In the context of AI-based lottery predictions, making informed decisions means understanding the limits of AI, the nature of randomness in lotteries, and the possible consequences of each choice.

Evaluating AI Predictions and Potential Risks

RISK ASSESSMENT IS a crucial aspect of interpreting AI-based lottery predictions. It requires a comprehensive understanding of the AI algorithms used and the probability rules at play. The complexity of AI systems can sometimes obscure the inherent risks involved in relying solely on their predictions. To avoid potential pitfalls, it is advisable to apply risk management principles when using AI for lottery predictions. This involves assessing the reliability of the AI system, the quality of data used, and the robustness of the algorithm. It is also important to consider external factors, such as changes in the lottery system rules or the introduction of new variables that could impact the prediction. By taking a comprehensive and cautious approach, one can navigate the uncertainties of AI predictions and make better-informed decisions in the lottery context.

Long-Term versus Short-Term Prediction Strategies: A Comparative Analysis

IN THE REALM OF AI-based lottery predictions, the choice between long-term and short-term strategies can significantly impact the prediction outcomes. Short-term strategies primarily focus on analyzing patterns in recent lottery draws, leveraging the immediacy of data for quick predictions. While these strategies can occasionally yield successful predictions, they are largely unreliable due to the inherent randomness of lottery draws.

On the other hand, long-term strategies involve a comprehensive analysis of historical lottery data over extended periods. Through deep learning algorithms, AI can detect subtle patterns and trends that are not immediately apparent. Such strategies yield more consistent results, offering a more reliable, though not infallible, basis for predictions.

However, neither approach can guarantee a winning outcome due to the unpredictable nature of lottery events. Therefore, the selection between short-term and long-term strategies should be guided by an understanding of their respective strengths and limitations, and an assessment of one's risk tolerance.

Harnessing the Power of Visualization Tools

VISUALIZATION TOOLS offer a unique way to interact with data, making it easier to analyze complex datasets and uncover insights that might otherwise remain hidden. In the context of AI-based lottery prediction, these tools could be instrumental in providing a more intuitive understanding of the patterns and trends unearthed from historical lottery data. The use of interactive charts, graphs, and heat maps can help to illustrate the frequency of occurrence of specific numbers, the commonality of number pairs or triplets, or even the spread of numbers over a given period. Moreover, visualization can help to identify anomalies or outliers in the data that might suggest potential opportunities for successful prediction. While the use of visualization tools cannot alter the inherent uncertainty of lottery outcomes, it can enhance one's understanding of the past behavior of lottery draws, thereby equipping players with valuable insights to inform their prediction strategies.

There are several online platforms that provide robust visualization tools, which can be utilized for analyzing lottery data. Some examples include:

- Tableau Public[1]: A free platform for data visualization, which can be used to create interactive charts and graphs.

- Google Data Studio[2]: This tool allows users to integrate data from various sources and create comprehensive reports and dashboards.

- D3.js[3]: A JavaScript library for creating dynamic, interactive data visualizations in web browsers.

---

1. https://public.tableau.com/en-us/s/gallery

2. https://datastudio.google.com/

3. https://d3js.org/

- Flourish[4]: A powerful data visualization and storytelling platform, with numerous templates available.

- Datawrapper[5]: An easy-to-use tool for creating interactive charts, maps, and tables.

REMEMBER, THE CHOICE of tool should be based on the specific requirements of the data visualization task, the complexity of the data, and the level of customization desired.

Understanding Misinterpretations and Avoiding Common Pitfalls

WHEN EMBARKING ON THE path of AI-based lottery prediction, it's vital to be aware of common misconceptions and pitfalls. A crucial misinterpretation is the belief that patterns derived from historical data can unerringly predict future outcomes. While AI and data analysis can unearth trends and patterns, the lottery is fundamentally a game of chance, and these patterns do not guarantee future results. Another common pitfall is the over-reliance on AI predictions without understanding the underlying assumptions or the nature of the data. This could lead to overconfidence and risky betting practices. On an ethically sensitive note, the use of AI in lottery predictions sparks debates around fairness and the alteration of a game of chance to one of computational advantage. It's essential to approach this area with a keen understanding of the limitations of AI, the nature of randomness, and a commitment to responsible gaming.

---

4. https://flourish.studio/examples

5. https://www.datawrapper.de/

Ensuring Accuracy: The Role of Cross-Referencing in AI Predictions

CROSS-REFERENCING AI predictions forms an essential part of establishing their reliability in predicting lottery outcomes. This process involves comparing predictions from different AI models or checking predictions against a separate source of truth to validate their accuracy. It's akin to having a second (or third) opinion in a medical diagnosis, thus providing a more holistic perspective. In the context of lottery predictions, cross-referencing can help calibrate AI models, identify potential biases, and ultimately improve their predictive performance. However, it's crucial to remember that while cross-referencing can enhance the robustness of AI predictions, it doesn't alter the inherent uncertainty of lottery outcomes. It is a tool for refining predictions, not guaranteeing winnings, and should be used responsibly within the framework of responsible gaming.

The Art of Prediction: Extracting Lessons from Successes and Failures

DRAWING INSIGHTS FROM both successful and unsuccessful predictions is an integral part of refining AI models and their predictive capabilities. Successes can highlight patterns that these models are correctly identifying, reinforcing their relevance in future predictions. However, failures can also provide valuable lessons, often uncovering overlooked data aspects or pointing to required adjustments in the model's algorithm. Hence, each prediction, regardless of its outcome, contributes to the model's learning. In addition, it assists in mitigating algorithmic bias, fine-tuning data interpretation, and improving overall predictive precision. However, the inherently random nature of lottery outcomes means that there will always be a degree of unpredictability that even the most advanced AI system cannot completely overcome. Therefore, it's crucial to maintain a balanced perspective, acknowledging both the capabilities and limitations of AI predictions in this context.

Understanding AI Predictions: The Perspective of Industry Professionals

INDUSTRY PROFESSIONALS interpret AI predictions in the lottery context with a mixture of skepticism and curiosity. They recognize the potential of AI in processing large data sets and identifying patterns humans may not discern. Professionals like data scientists and statisticians appreciate the potential of AI in enhancing the accuracy of predictions. However, they also caution against over-reliance on these predictions, citing the inherent randomness in lottery draws. This balance between the promise of AI and the unpredictability of lotteries keeps the industry grounded, serving as a reminder that while technology can provide tools for understanding, it is not an infallible solution. In the end, professionals agree that the use of AI in predicting lottery outcomes should be approached with responsible innovation, ensuring that the technology's benefits do not overshadow the ethical and legal considerations in its application.

Chapter 13: Strategies for Diverse Lottery Games

I n chapter 13, we delve into various strategies that can be employed across diverse lottery games, exploring how the application of AI intersects with these strategies. This chapter provides an analytical overview of the range of lottery games available worldwide, each with their unique set of rules and odds. From conventional number draws to instant win scratch cards, the diversity in lottery games presents a wide, dynamic field for the application of AI predictions. We will dissect notable examples, scrutinizing how AI can be implemented to analyze patterns and trends in different types of games. While understanding that AI cannot guarantee lottery wins, we will explore the potential of AI in possibly increasing the odds of winning by forecasting patterns with greater precision than random guessing. As we navigate through these strategies, we will also continually underscore the importance of responsible use of AI, mindful of the ethical and legal implications. So, keep an open mind as we embark on this fascinating journey, where mathematics, technology, and chance intersect.

Adapting AI Strategies to Diverse Game Rules

IN THE WORLD OF LOTTERY games, each type of game comes with its own set of rules, thus requiring different strategies when attempting to predict outcomes. These variations pose challenges and opportunities for AI application. AI, with its ability to process large datasets and identify patterns, holds potential for adapting to different game rules. This adaptability stems from AI's capacity to learn from past data and adjust its algorithms accordingly. For instance, in number draw games, AI could potentially analyze historical draw data to predict likely number combinations. Conversely, for instant win games, AI might scrutinize patterns in prize distribution. However, it's crucial to remember that while AI can potentially increase the odds of winning, it does not guarantee a win. It provides an edge, not a guarantee. Also, the ethical and legal implications of using AI in lottery predictions should always be given utmost consideration.

The Impact of Geographic Factors on Lottery Strategies

GEOGRAPHIC FACTORS play a non-trivial role in shaping lottery strategies. In many jurisdictions, the rules of the lottery games may differ, thus requiring a nuanced understanding and application of AI-based prediction techniques. For instance, some regions may have games with a larger pool of numbers from which the winning numbers are drawn. These variations significantly influence the prediction models, necessitating alterations in the AI algorithms. Additionally, the availability and completeness of historical draw data, which serve as the foundation for AI's predictive analysis, can vary geographically. Therefore, acknowledging and accommodating these geographic considerations is crucial to the effectiveness and accuracy of AI in lottery outcome prediction. It also reinforces the principle of responsible AI use, taking into account the specific context and constraints of different regions.

The Intricacies of Predicting Multi-State and National Lotteries

MULTI-STATE AND NATIONAL lotteries present a unique challenge for AI-based prediction. The vast scale of these lotteries, coupled with the astronomical number of potential number combinations, significantly complicates the prediction process. AI software has to analyze a much larger dataset, and the predictive algorithms need to be exceptionally sophisticated to discern any meaningful patterns. Additionally, these lotteries often have complex rules and structures, such as powerball numbers or bonus balls, that require distinct treatment within the prediction model. Furthermore, the infrequent nature of draws in many national lotteries means that historical data is less abundant, potentially limiting the effectiveness of AI-based predictions. Therefore, while AI can offer some insights in this context, the considerable complexity and scale of multi-state and national lotteries mean that its predictive capabilities are more constrained than in smaller-scale games.

The Complexities of Predicting Outcomes in Online Lottery Games

ONLINE LOTTERY GAMES introduce additional variables into the already complex equation of prediction. Unlike traditional lotteries, these games are not bound by geographical borders, and draws may occur more frequently, leading to a larger volume of historical data for AI to analyze. Moreover, online lottery platforms often have unique rules and game structures, creating an entirely new set of patterns for AI to detect and learn from. However, the increased accessibility and frequency of these games can also lead to a surge in players, further inflating the number of potential number combinations and intensifying the prediction challenge. Thus, while online lottery games open up new possibilities for AI-based prediction, they also present their own set of intricacies that necessitate advanced, adaptable algorithms.

AI-Powered Lottery Strategies: Insights from Evidence

WHILE THE TASK OF PREDICTING lottery outcomes remains an immense challenge, there have been several intriguing attempts to leverage AI in this pursuit, each offering valuable insights. For instance, a syndicate from MIT used a combination of statistical analysis and strategic ticket buying to win the Massachusetts Lottery multiple times, earning millions in the process. They capitalized on a loophole in the game mechanics, which allowed them to secure a positive expected return when the jackpot reached a certain threshold. In another case, an individual used a rudimentary form of machine learning to predict minor prizes in a local lottery game, demonstrating the potential for AI to augment human intuition and analysis. However, it remains to be seen whether these techniques can scale up to larger, more complex games, and whether they can consistently perform better than random chance. Moreover, the ethical implications of such strategies are contentious, raising concerns about fairness, gambling addiction, and the potential for exploitation or fraud.

A Comparative Study of Lottery Strategies: Human Intuition Versus AI Predictions

WHEN COMPARING TRADITIONAL lottery strategies to AI-powered approaches, the contrast is marked. Traditional strategies often rely on the player's intuition or historical data and may include methods such as playing 'hot' numbers that appear frequently, or 'cold' numbers that are overdue. These methods, while sometimes successful, do not have a consistent track record of predicting lottery outcomes accurately.

On the other hand, AI-based strategies take a more systematic approach. They leverage machine learning and complex algorithms to analyze vast amounts of data, including previous winning numbers, time patterns, and even the specific mechanics of different lottery games. In this regard, they offer a more statistical and potentially reliable method of prediction.

However, it is essential to note that despite their apparent sophistication, AI strategies are not foolproof. They have their limitations and ethical implications, as already discussed. The ever-changing nature of lottery games, coupled with their inherent randomness, presents a significant challenge, even to the most advanced AI. Therefore, while AI strategies may hold promise for the future, they should be used responsibly and ethically, and players should approach them with realistic expectations.

The Role of Collaborative Tactics: Exploring Lottery Pools and Syndicates

LOTTERY POOLS AND SYNDICATES represent another popular approach to lottery participation, one that is inherently social and collaborative. In essence, these tactics involve a group of individuals collectively buying a larger number of lottery tickets, thereby increasing their chances of winning. The cost of the tickets and any winnings are typically shared proportionally among the participants.

This method does not attempt to predict the numbers that will be drawn; instead, it is a strategic play on probability, with larger ticket volumes increasing the likelihood of holding a winning ticket. Despite this, the randomness of the lottery means that even with a large number of tickets, a win is never guaranteed.

Similar to AI predictions, pools and syndicates also come with their share of challenges and considerations. On a practical level, managing a lottery pool or syndicate can be complex, demanding clear communication and transparency to avoid disputes. More fundamentally, this approach also raises questions around the equitable distribution of winnings, and the potential for exploitation or disagreements among participants. Thus, while pooling or syndicate strategies may enhance the social aspect of lottery participation and improve odds, they need to be approached with careful planning and a clear understanding of the implications.

Special Events: An Examination of Raffles and Millionaire Draws

DISTINCT FROM CONVENTIONAL lottery games, special events such as raffles and millionaire draws hold their unique appeal. These events often come with a guaranteed top prize, and the odds of winning are usually better due to a limited number of tickets being sold. Raffles, for instance, operate on a draw system with set prizes, while millionaire draws promise hefty cash prizes or sometimes non-cash rewards like properties or luxury cars. Although these events can seem more enticing, one should bear in mind that, much like traditional lottery games, they are still games of chance. As such, the outcome of these draws remains unpredictable, even with the sophisticated capabilities of artificial intelligence. This unpredictability underlines the thrill and allure of these games, all while reinforcing the need for responsible participation. It's important to remember that no matter the game, a win is never guaranteed.

Comparing Lottery Formats: A Statistical Examination

WHEN DEALING WITH DIFFERENT lottery formats, a statistical analysis can provide valuable insights into the underlying structures and chances of winning. Each lottery format has its unique set of rules and prize distributions, and hence, different probabilities associated with each prize tier. For instance, a traditional draw-based lottery that requires matching six out of 49 numbers will have different odds compared to a lottery where players choose five numbers out of 39.

Similarly, special events such as raffles and millionaire draws have their unique statistical properties, often involving a fixed number of tickets and guaranteed prizes. However, no matter the type or format, the results of these lotteries are essentially random. While artificial intelligence can analyze past data for pattern recognition, the inherently unpredictable nature of these games remains. This unpredictability is a crucial factor to bear in mind for all lottery participants, reinforcing the importance of responsible play.

Artificial intelligence can, however, provide some insight into the frequency of certain outcomes, albeit without the guarantee of future predictions. Regardless of the format, the mathematical principle remains: the outcome of any random event cannot be accurately predicted on an individual basis.

Exploring Diverse Lottery Games: A Strategy to Increase Winning Probability

A NOTABLE TACTIC TO improve one's odds in the lottery is to participate in a variety of games. By diversifying their ticket portfolio, players can tap into the different probability structures that each lottery format offers. For example, smaller local lotteries may have fewer participants resulting in higher winning odds. Simultaneously, participating in larger, national lotteries offers the chance to win significantly larger jackpots, albeit with lower winning probabilities. Similarly, instant win games may have smaller payouts but higher overall odds of winning some prize. This diversified approach to playing lottery games, therefore, serves as a strategy to maximize potential wins and spread risk. However, it is important to remember that this does not guarantee a win; it is merely a method to increase chances of winning while ensuring responsible play. Remember, the core principle of lotteries holds: they are games of chance, and their outcomes are fundamentally unpredictable.

Chapter 14: Risk and Reward Management

The beauty of lottery games lies in their unpredictability, offering a thrill that stems from the potent mix of risk and reward. As we embark on the fourteenth chapter, 'Risk and Reward Management', we delve deeper into this precarious balance between potential gains and losses. This chapter aims to explore the interplay of risk and reward in the context of lottery games, unraveling the inherent risk associated with playing these games and the potential rewards that beckon players worldwide. We will discuss risk management strategies that can be adopted by players to regulate their investments in lottery games, making sure they are not exceeding their means in the pursuit of elusive riches. Alongside this, we will consider the emotional rewards and psychological impacts of these games. Despite the low probability of winning, the allure of a potential life-changing win drives millions to participate. Understanding this dichotomy between the actual odds and the perceived rewards is essential to unpacking the enduring appeal of lottery games. Remember, the true essence of these games is not merely about winning or losing; it's about understanding the journey of risk and reward that each ticket takes you on. As with the previous chapters, the role of artificial intelligence (AI) will be at the forefront of our discussion, providing insights into how technology can illuminate the nuances of this risk-reward balance.

Understanding Financial Management in

Gambling

FINANCIAL MANAGEMENT in gambling is a crucial factor often overlooked by many players. It revolves around setting a budget for gambling activities and strictly adhering to it, irrespective of wins or losses. The principle is to ensure that players only gamble with money they can afford to lose, thereby minimizing potential financial distress. It's noteworthy that the exhilaration of gambling often clouds players' judgment, leading to reckless spending beyond their means. This is where the role of responsible financial management becomes paramount. By setting a predefined gambling budget and tracking spending, players can enjoy the thrill of the game without jeopardizing their financial stability.

Artificial intelligence can aid in this endeavor, offering tools to track and alert players about their spending patterns. Some AI systems can even predict players' behavior based on their past activity, potentially identifying risky behavior before it spirals out of control. However, the implementation of such technology raises questions around privacy and personal autonomy, necessitating a careful balance between protective measures and individual rights. These are considerations we will explore further in the subsequent sections.

Balancing the Budget for Lottery Play

TO MANAGE A BUDGET successfully for lottery play, it requires a clear understanding of one's financial limits and the inherent unpredictability of the game. Players must set aside a dedicated amount for lottery tickets, ensuring this amount does not interfere with essential expenses such as bills, groceries, mortgage payments, or any other financial obligations. Once the budget is set, it's crucial to adhere to it strictly, resisting the temptation to spend more after a loss or even a win. The allure of a potential jackpot win should not cloud sound financial judgment.

Artificial intelligence tools can play an integral role in this process, providing analytics and insights into spending patterns. These tools can help players stay within their budget, send alerts when spending approaches the set limit, and even offer projections of potential future spending based on past behavior. Nonetheless, the integration of AI into financial management for lottery play must be done responsibly, taking into account the ethical concerns of privacy and autonomy. As we delve deeper into this intriguing intersection of technology and gambling, it becomes evident that a careful balance must be struck between the use of AI and the preservation of human agency and decision-making.

The Gambler's Fallacy: A Misunderstanding of Probability

THE GAMBLER'S FALLACY, also known as the Monte Carlo fallacy, is a common misconception related to probability and chance. This fallacy is based on the mistaken belief that if something occurs more frequently than normal during a particular period, it will happen less frequently in the future, or vice versa. In the context of lottery play, this can lead to flawed strategies, such as believing that a number that hasn't been drawn for a while is 'due' to appear or that a recently drawn number won't show up again soon. However, in a truly random process like a lottery draw, each event is independent; the outcome of one draw has no effect on future draws. Artificial intelligence, albeit powerful in modeling complex patterns, cannot undo the inherent randomness of such events. Thus, it is essential for players to understand the concept of the gambler's fallacy to avoid falling into this trap of flawed reasoning.

The Science of Betting: AI-Driven Techniques and Strategies

SMART BETTING INVOLVES leveraging data analysis and predictive models to optimize the odds of winning. With the advancements in Artificial Intelligence (AI), these techniques and strategies have evolved significantly. AI-based algorithms can analyze vast amounts of historical lottery data, identifying patterns that may seem invisible to the human eye. However, these patterns do not guarantee winnings as lottery outcomes are fundamentally random. They can only help in making more informed decisions, increasing the chances of success slightly over pure guesswork. It's crucial to remember that while AI can enhance strategic betting, it does not promise certain victory. Responsible gambling still requires players to bet within their means and to be aware of the risks involved.

Understanding the Gambler's Psyche: Navigating Emotions for Responsible Betting

THE PSYCHOLOGY OF GAMBLING involves a complex interplay of cognitive, emotional, and behavioral factors. It is crucial to maintain a clear mind when engaging in betting activities, as emotional decision-making can lead to impulsive and potentially harmful choices. Cognitive biases often mislead players into overestimating their chances of winning, while the thrill of potential gains can cloud judgement. It's important to approach gambling with a sense of reality, acknowledging the high risks involved and the statistical improbability of significant wins. Responsible betting involves setting limits on time and money spent, understanding the game thoroughly, and being prepared for losses. When gambling ceases to be entertaining and starts causing stress, it may be time to reevaluate one's involvement. Ultimately, maintaining a balanced perspective towards gambling can cultivate healthier habits and prevent the development of gambling-related problems.

High-Risk Versus Low-Risk Betting Strategies: Evaluating the Pros and Cons

HIGH-RISK AND LOW-RISK betting strategies each have their distinct advantages and drawbacks. High-risk strategies typically involve placing larger bets on less likely outcomes, which can yield high payoffs but also increase the chances of losing substantially. On the other hand, low-risk strategies generally involve placing smaller bets on more likely outcomes, yielding smaller payoffs but reducing the likelihood of significant losses.

The choice between high-risk and low-risk betting greatly depends on the individual's risk tolerance, financial capacity, and knowledge of the game. A well-informed and disciplined approach is critical in both cases. High-risk betting can be exciting and potentially rewarding, but the potential for substantial loss is a significant factor to consider. Similarly, while low-risk betting may offer a safer route, it requires patience and a strict adherence to set limits.

In the context of AI, these strategies could be subject to more nuanced decision-making based on predictive models and historical data analysis. However, the core principles of responsible betting still apply. It's essential to remember that betting, whether high-risk or low-risk, should be approached responsibly, with full understanding of the potential outcomes and consequences.

Capitalizing on Wins: Maximizing the Reward System Through AI

THE REWARD SYSTEM IN betting is inherently tied with the strategy employed. In both high-risk and low-risk betting, a win is the reward for a well-played strategy. Capitalizing on these wins, however,

AI AND THE LOTTERY: DEFYING ODDS WITH
INTELLIGENT PREDICTION   143

requires a deeper understanding of the odds, the game, and patterns that may exist. In the realm of artificial intelligence, the possibility of identifying such patterns becomes plausible due to the high processing power and capability of AI to analyze large datasets. By utilizing AI, bettors can potentially increase their chance of winning by leveraging historical data and predictive models. However, it's crucial to maintain a realistic understanding of the limitations of such models and the inherent unpredictability of betting outcomes. Even with the aid of AI, betting remains a game of chance, with wins and losses part of the process. Responsible betting, therefore, must always be the cornerstone of every strategy, with the knowledge that capitalizing on wins is as much about understanding when to bet as it is about knowing when to walk away.

Expert Risk Management: Navigating the Betting Landscape with Professional Insight

RISK MANAGEMENT IS a fundamental aspect of any betting strategy and professionals approach this with a deep understanding of the game's dynamics and their betting models. Experts consider variables like bet size, betting frequency, and the odds to determine the risk level. By setting betting limits, they control potential losses, demonstrating the importance of discipline in betting. They also diversify their bets, spreading the risk and mitigating potential losses, a strategy akin to diversifying an investment portfolio. The use of AI tools enters the picture as an additional layer of analysis, helping predict possible outcomes based on historical data and trends. However, professionals know that AI doesn't guarantee a win; it's simply another tool to inform their decisions. Ultimately, expert risk management in betting is a delicate balance of mathematical strategy, intuition, discipline, and responsible decision-making.

Maintaining Self-Control: Ensuring Responsible Betting Practices

AN ESSENTIAL ASPECT of betting that is often overlooked is the need for self-management to avoid addictive behavior. It is easy to get caught up in the thrill of the gamble, but maintaining self-control is crucial to ensure that betting remains a leisure activity and not a compulsive habit. It's important to set personal limits – be it in terms of time spent betting or the financial amount committed to bets. It's also helpful to take regular breaks and to understand that no strategy, not even those bolstered by AI, can guarantee a win every time. Constant self-monitoring for signs of addictive behavior can prove beneficial in maintaining a healthy relationship with betting. Ultimately, while AI can provide useful insights and predictive analytics, the responsibility for making informed and balanced decisions rests with the individual.

Responsible Financial Planning: Utilizing Lottery Winnings as a Stepping Stone

WHILE THE PROSPECT of winning the lottery can be thrilling, it's important to approach the potential windfall with a level-headed, long-term view. Lottery winnings, no matter how large, can dwindle quickly if not managed responsibly. Therefore, it's crucial to consider these funds as a stepping stone towards sound financial planning rather than an end in itself. Invest a portion of the winnings in diverse asset classes - equities, bonds, real estate, or even a small business. This approach not only ensures growth of the capital but also provides steady income streams. Just as AI aids in discerning lottery trends, a financial adviser can help navigate investment strategies, balancing risk and reward based on individual financial goals and circumstances. Ultimately, the real win lies not in the immediate gratification of a lottery victory, but in the lasting security and prosperity that wise financial management can bring.

Chapter 15: Beyond Number Picking – AI for Comprehensive Strategy

In Chapter 15, we delve into the vast possibilities that extend beyond the primary application of AI in lottery games - number picking. We introduce the concept of using AI for comprehensive strategic planning. In this context, AI doesn't merely serve as a tool to predict which numbers might come up in the next draw. Instead, it becomes an integral part of a broader strategy, helping to manage and analyze data, optimize betting, and ultimately, maximize returns while minimizing risk. This chapter sheds light on how AI can be used to intelligently strategize betting actions, taking into account factors such as frequency of betting, amount bet on each game, choosing the appropriate lottery game, and more. By the end of this chapter, you will understand that winning at lottery games doesn't always mean hitting the jackpot – sometimes, it's about strategically playing the game to turn the odds in your favor.

As discussed in previous chapters, AI is a powerful tool for predicting lottery outcomes. However, its capabilities do not end there. With the right algorithms and data processing techniques, AI can be used to analyze a variety of factors that influence the outcome of lottery games. This includes historical data on winning numbers, player demographics, ticket sales, and more.

By taking a holistic approach to AI in lotteries, it becomes possible to make smarter decisions when it comes to betting. For example, analyzing historical data can reveal patterns and trends that can guide players towards more profitable games. Similarly, understanding player demographics can help tailor marketing strategies and promotions to attract a wider audience.

Making the Most of AI: Choosing the Right Moment to Play

THE TIMING OF WHEN to participate in a lottery can significantly affect the potential return on investment. AI can help predict optimal play times by analyzing various influencing factors. For instance, it can analyze ticket buying trends to identify when fewer people are participating in a particular lottery draw. This reduction in competition can increase the chance of winning. Moreover, AI can conduct a performance analysis of different lottery games at different times, enabling players to choose the most opportune moments to participate. Hence, timing strategies guided by AI could prove to be a game-changer in the world of lottery games, adding an additional layer of sophistication to betting strategies and potentially improving players' odds of success.

To harness the power of AI in timing your lottery participation, you would need to put into play a combination of data gathering, data cleaning, model selection, training, testing, and prediction execution. To begin, you'd need to collect and clean historical lottery data, including past winning numbers, time of draws, and player participation levels. This data can typically be found on official lottery websites or through third-party vendors.

Then, you would select an appropriate machine learning model for your data. This could be a time series forecasting model, such as Auto-Regressive Integrated Moving Average (ARIMA), or a more complex neural network like Long Short-Term Memory (LSTM). The chosen model should then be trained on a portion of the historical data, tested on a different portion, and fine-tuned to achieve the best performance. The final step involves deploying the model to start making predictions on when is the best time to participate in a lottery draw.

It's important to remember that while AI can increase your chances, it doesn't guarantee a win. Lotteries, by their nature, are games of chance and the outcomes are ultimately random. AI merely provides an informed strategy to optimize your participation.

Analyzing Lottery Jackpot Trends With AI

ARTIFICIAL INTELLIGENCE offers a compelling tool for analyzing lottery jackpot trends. It can dig deep into historical data to detect patterns and correlations that might be missed by the human eye. For instance, AI can identify if there are specific periods where jackpots are more likely to be claimed, or if there are any cyclical patterns associated with jackpot amounts. More advanced AI systems can even consider external factors such as economic indicators or social events, potentially revealing hidden influences on jackpot trends. It's important to note that these observations and predictions are probabilistic, not certain. Nevertheless, this kind of detailed analysis can provide lottery participants with valuable information, allowing them to make more informed decisions about when and how to play. However, the use of AI in this context also raises significant ethical and legal concerns that cannot be overlooked, such as the fairness of these sophisticated strategies and their potential to disrupt the random nature of lottery games.

Integrating Diverse Data Points for Comprehensive Analysis

THE INTEGRATION OF diverse data points allows for a comprehensive analysis of lottery trends. By leveraging AI, we can truly harness the full potential of the vast datasets available. The technique involves incorporating various elements such as the timing of draws, historical jackpot values, winner demographics, and even seemingly unrelated data like weather patterns or global events. This kind of multifaceted assessment helps in refining the predictions, factoring in the influence that these diverse elements may have on lottery outcomes. By converting these disparate data points into actionable insights, AI provides an analytical edge that can enhance strategic planning for lottery participation. However, as we delve deeper into this level of analysis, we must remain aware of the ethical implications and ensure that our methods promote fairness and transparency.

Making the Right Choice: Understanding Game Selection Strategies

SELECTING WHICH LOTTERY game to play is a significant decision for participants, often dictated by a variety of factors. It's not merely a game of chance, but a calculated move influenced by prize pools, odds of winning, ticket prices, and the participant's risk tolerance. AI can assist in this decision-making process by analyzing past data of different games, identifying patterns, and predicting outcomes. For instance, some games may consistently yield smaller but more frequent wins, while others offer larger jackpots but with less probability of winning. By factoring in these parameters, AI can provide insights that help participants align their game selection with their individual goals and risk appetite. Nevertheless, while AI can guide these decisions, it's essential to remember that the ultimate choice rests with the participant, and the unpredictability of lottery outcomes always adds an element of surprise and excitement to the game.

Steps to Choosing the Right Lottery Game

with AI Assistance

1. **Identify Your Goals:** The first step involves introspection. Do you favor a lower risk game with smaller, more frequent wins, or are you a high-risk player aiming for the jackpot? Your personal goals will play a significant role in game selection.

1. **Understand the Game Parameters:** Familiarize yourself with the various parameters of the lottery games available. This includes understanding the prize pools, odds of winning, and ticket prices.

1. **Leverage AI for Pattern Identification:** Utilize an AI tool to analyze past data from the games you're interested in. The AI can identify patterns, such as the frequency of wins or the average win size, which can provide insights into the game's performance over time.

1. **Analyze AI Predictions:** Consider the AI's predictions based on data analysis. Use these insights to understand which game might align with your goals and risk tolerance.

1. **Make an Informed Decision:** Armed with your personal goals, understanding of the game parameters, and AI insights, make your game selection. Remember, while AI can guide your decision, the ultimate choice is yours. Embrace the unpredictability of the game and enjoy the element of surprise it brings.

Balancing Entry Frequency for Optimal Participation

PARTICIPATION FREQUENCY in the lottery is a key factor that has significant bearing on your likelihood of winning. The more regularly you participate, the higher the accumulative chances you have to secure a win. However, this must be balanced against the cost of participation and the risk of potential losses. It's essential to recognize that while participating more often statistically increases your chances of winning, each draw is an independent event, and winning is not guaranteed. Utilizing AI can help in understanding the potential impact of participation frequency on your overall returns. For instance, the AI tool might analyze historical data to determine if there are any patterns related to frequency of participation and winning outcomes. The insights gained can inform your participation strategy, helping you optimize your frequency of entries while keeping in line with your risk tolerance and financial capabilities.

Group Play and Syndicates: Optimizing Lottery Participation with AI

ENGAGING IN GROUP PLAY or becoming part of a syndicate is another strategy often utilized by lottery participants. By pooling resources, group members can afford to buy more lottery tickets, thus increasing their collective chances of winning. AI can play a pivotal role in these collaborative ventures, particularly in managing and distributing the pooled funds optimally, and analyzing potential winning combinations based on historical data.

AI can also aid in establishing a fair distribution of winnings among syndicate members. Using predictive algorithms, AI can generate numerous potential scenarios and their outcomes, thereby allowing syndicate members to have a clear and transparent understanding of their respective shares in case of a win. Further, AI can streamline the process of choosing the number combinations to play, adding a layer of strategic decision-making to the otherwise random nature of lottery games.

However, while AI can significantly enhance the efficiency and strategic depth of group play in lotteries, it's crucial to remember that the random nature of these games means a guaranteed win is still out of reach. As with all forms of gambling, responsible play should be the guiding principle for syndicates as well.

Leveraging AI for Special Draw Strategies

SPECIAL DRAWS IN THE lottery world are events that offer enhanced prizes or higher chances of winning. These events typically occur on notable dates or anniversaries, creating a sense of anticipation and excitement among lottery players. AI can be used effectively in these situations to strategize and predict potential outcomes. Through trend analysis and pattern recognition of previous special draws, AI can identify patterns that might hint at probable winning combinations. These insights can help players make informed decisions about the numbers they choose to play. Additionally, AI can forecast the likelihood of certain numbers being drawn based on past data, allowing players to strategically choose their numbers for the special draw. However, it's important to note that while AI can provide valuable insights and enhance strategic planning, the ultimate outcome of a lottery draw remains inherently unpredictable.

The Role of AI in Long-Term Lottery Strategy

IN ADDITION TO IMMEDIATE strategy for special draws, AI can be instrumental in developing long-term strategic plans for lottery play. AI's ability to sift through vast datasets and identify subtle patterns and trends makes it a powerful tool in predicting potential winning combinations over a prolonged period. It can analyze years of lottery data, discern the frequency of individual numbers being drawn, and offer statistical probabilities for future draws. Moreover, AI can facilitate a more systematic approach to lottery play by enabling players to consistently apply their chosen strategies over time, rather than changing tactics on a draw-by-draw basis. This kind of systematized approach can potentially increase the chances of success in the long run. However, as always with lottery games, luck remains a significant factor, and the predictions made by AI should be used as guidance rather than a guarantee of success.

Impact of AI on Lottery Results: A Deeper Dive

THE TRANSFORMATIVE role of AI in lottery strategy extends beyond individual players and engulfs the entire landscape of chance-based games. Let's consider the case of a renowned data scientist who, through the application of machine learning algorithms, developed a model that could predict lottery outcomes with a marginally higher success rate than pure chance. While this didn't guarantee a win each time, it significantly increased the probability of success over multiple attempts. Similarly, a tech startup leveraged AI's predictive capabilities to create a lottery forecasting app, which attracted thousands of users globally and sparked widespread debate about the use of technology in chance-based games. These stories underline the potential of AI in reshaping our approach to games of chance, yet simultaneously caution against over-reliance on technology, highlighting the persistent role of luck and the ethical boundaries that must be respected.

The Case of the Bulgarian Lottery Incident: An AI Perspective

IN AN INTRIGUING REAL-world example, the Bulgarian lottery drew the same six numbers in two consecutive draws in 2008, a statistical phenomenon that sparked significant public interest and skepticism. Given the odds are roughly 1 in 13,983,816 for such an event, it was initially believed that there must have been some fraudulent intervention. However, after a rigorous investigation, it was confirmed to be a genuinely random occurrence.

This incident provides fertile ground for the application of AI. If an AI model had been built using previous draw data, it could have calculated the probability of such an event occurring and estimated the likelihood of it happening again in the future. While it wouldn't necessarily predict the exact numbers, it could have provided some valuable insight into the potential for such statistically rare events. This case encapsulates the essence of the opportunity and limitations of using AI in predicting lottery outcomes. It underscores the reality that, despite advanced technology, the element of chance and unpredictability remains a defining characteristic of lottery games.

Chapter 16: The Future of AI in Lottery Prediction

As we delve into Chapter 16: The Future of AI in Lottery Prediction, we turn our gaze towards the horizon, where the unpredictable dance of chance meets the relentless march of technology. This chapter seeks to explore the tantalizing potential of what AI could bring to the world of lottery prediction, while simultaneously acknowledging the uncertainties and ethical considerations that such advancements bring with them.

We will discuss the potential improvements in AI capabilities, the development of more sophisticated models capable of processing vast amounts of data, and the potential these advancements hold for predicting the inherently unpredictable nature of lottery draws. As technology continues to evolve, so too does the scope for prediction models and their accuracy. Could AI, as it grows and learns, start to see patterns where humans cannot?

We will also consider the ethical and legal implications of AI in lottery prediction. As AI becomes increasingly sophisticated, questions arise about the fairness of using such tools in a game that has always been considered a game of chance. Moreover, what would be the societal impacts should AI become the ultimate tool for predicting lottery outcomes?

Finally, we will ponder the implications for the lottery industry itself. How might the use of AI for prediction affect the appeal of the lottery, its regulation, and its role in society? These are some of the thought-provoking questions we aim to address in this chapter.

So, fasten your seat belts as we journey into the uncharted territory of the future, exploring the fascinating intersection between artificial intelligence and the age-old game of chance. As we move forward, remember that at its core, the lottery is a dance with chance, and even with the most sophisticated AI, certainty remains elusive.

Advancements in the AI Landscape

AS WE STEP INTO THE era of artificial intelligence, we are witnessing an exponential growth in computational power and data generation. These advancements have facilitated the development of complex algorithms that are capable of learning from and making predictions based on massive datasets. AI's potential to process and analyze these vast amounts of data far surpasses human capabilities, paving the way for breakthrough innovations in numerous fields, including the lottery industry. The unprecedented ability of AI to detect subtle patterns within large datasets may hint at its potential to predict outcomes of random events like lottery draws. However, this potential is tempered by the recognition that such events are, by nature, intended to be inherently unpredictable. Furthermore, the integration of AI in such contexts raises pertinent questions regarding its ethical, legal, and societal implications, which need to be addressed to ensure responsible and fair use of this powerful technology.

The Power of Predictive Analytics in Forecasting

IN THE REALM OF FORECASTING, predictive analytics has emerged as a game-changer, elevating our ability to extrapolate future outcomes based on past data. Utilizing techniques such as data mining, statistics, modeling, machine learning, and artificial intelligence, predictive analytics can assess historical data to predict future trends. In the context of lottery predictions, this means analyzing past lottery draw results to identify patterns. However, the inherent randomness of lottery draws presents a formidable challenge to predictive analytics. It's important to note that while these advanced methods can potentially enhance our understanding of trends and increase the accuracy of forecasts, they cannot guarantee absolute certainty, especially in inherently unpredictable domains such as lottery outcomes. As we continue to explore the integration of AI and predictive analytics into the lottery industry, it is crucial that we maintain a balanced perspective, acknowledging the potential of these technologies while remaining cognizant of their limitations and the ethical implications of their use.

Embracing the Convergence of AI with Emerging Technologies

THE FUSION OF AI WITH emerging technologies promises a new realm of possibilities, extending beyond the traditional boundaries of predictive analytics. Blockchain technology, for instance, with its immutable and transparent nature, can be used in conjunction with AI to enhance transparency and trust in predictive systems like lottery forecasting. On the other hand, Quantum computing, with its ability to handle vast amounts of data and complex calculations in significantly less time, may pave the way for more sophisticated prediction models. However, these advancements are not without their challenges. Questions around scalability, integration, security, and ethical implications come to the fore as we delve deeper into these uncharted territories. It is paramount to conduct thorough research and maintain rigorous regulatory oversight to ensure that the convergence of these technologies with AI leads to outcomes that are beneficial for society as a whole while minimizing any potential risks.

The Implications of Virtual Reality and Simulations in Predictive Models

BEYOND THE SCOPE OF blockchain and quantum computing, another significant technological frontier that holds promise in the realm of predictive analytics is Virtual Reality (VR) and simulation technology. These technologies, while typically associated with fields like gaming and entertainment, carry significant potential for applications in the arena of predictive modeling. By creating immersive, interactive environments, VR and simulation technology can provide detailed, multi-dimensional representations of complex systems. This can be leveraged to create more sophisticated predictive models, which account for a multitude of variables and their interactions. For instance, in the context of lottery predictions, a VR-based simulation could map out thousands of possible outcomes based on a vast array of factors, enabling AI algorithms to analyze these scenarios and identify patterns or trends. Yet, as with other technological advancements, the integration of VR and simulations into predictive analytics brings its own set of challenges. Issues such as data privacy, ethical use of simulations, and the risk of creating misleading representations warrant careful consideration.

The Intersection of Legislation and Technological Innovation

THE INTERPLAY BETWEEN legislation and AI in the lottery industry is a complex and nuanced topic. As these two spheres converge, a host of legal, ethical, and societal questions come to the fore. Legislative bodies are faced with the task of developing regulations that strike a balance between fostering technological innovation and protecting consumers. For instance, the use of AI in predicting lottery outcomes may be seen as an unfair advantage, prompting legal authorities to scrutinize such practices. Similarly, ensuring the ethical use of personal data for AI algorithms presents a significant legislative challenge. On the other hand, overly restrictive regulations may stifle the growth and innovation in AI technologies. As such, lawmakers must tread a fine line between protecting the interests of society, ensuring fair competition, and encouraging the advancement of technology.

The globalization of AI lottery strategies extends the reach and impact of this innovative approach beyond the borders of individual nations. Technology does not operate in isolation, but rather in a global context where innovations in one area can rapidly influence and be adapted in others. In the context of lottery strategies, AI has the potential to transcend geographical barriers, offering a universal method for predicting lottery outcomes that can be applied across different lottery systems worldwide. However, this widespread adoption of AI lottery strategies also necessitates a global conversation surrounding the ethical use of such technologies. The international community must collaborate on creating universally accepted guidelines to ensure the responsible use of AI in lottery prediction, balancing the pursuit of technological advancements with safeguarding ethical standards and promoting fair play.

Impact on Social Dynamics and Emerging Trends in Communal Gaming

IN RECENT YEARS, THE trend towards communal gaming has been spurred by advances in technology, including AI. This shift is fundamentally altering the social dynamics of gaming, including the lottery. The introduction of AI in lottery prediction not only changes the individual approach to gaming but also paves the way for collective strategies. Communities of gamers can pool their resources to leverage AI's predictive capabilities, increasing their combined chances of winning. This not only democratizes access to winning strategies but also fosters a sense of camaraderie and teamwork among players. However, such trends also present new challenges in ensuring fairness and legality. As communal gaming becomes increasingly popular, regulatory bodies must adapt to these changes, devising guidelines that promote ethical gaming practices while accommodating the innovative use of AI.

Advancing AI's Predictive Abilities: The Road Ahead

ARTIFICIAL INTELLIGENCE is poised to revolutionize the lottery industry, with cutting-edge predictive algorithms showing increasing potential. The next step in enhancing AI's predictive capabilities is refining algorithms to handle the inherent randomness of lottery drawings. This involves acquiring large datasets of historical lottery outcomes and using sophisticated machine learning techniques to discern potential patterns. Alongside this, it is essential to improve AI's ability to adapt to changes in lottery rules and formats, thereby ensuring its predictive models remain robust and versatile. However, the advancement of AI's predictive capabilities must always be tempered by a commitment to ethical use. As we tread the fine line between innovative progress and responsible gaming, it's crucial to maintain a dialogue with regulatory bodies, fostering an environment wherein AI can thrive without jeopardizing the integrity of communal gaming.

Enhancing Security and Ethical Practices in AI

AS AI TECHNOLOGIES infiltrate the lottery industry, security and ethical considerations take center stage. On one hand, AI presents an opportunity to bolster security efforts. Utilizing advanced machine learning algorithms, AI can identify potential fraudulent activities or irregular patterns more effectively than traditional methods. On the other hand, implementing AI raises new ethical questions. As data is the lifeblood of AI systems, privacy and data protection become major concerns. The use of AI also amplifies the responsibility of lottery organizations to ensure fair play. As we navigate this new landscape, it's imperative that we establish robust security measures and ethical guidelines. This involves safeguarding personal data, ensuring the transparency of AI operations, maintaining algorithmic fairness, and promoting responsible gaming. The evolution of AI in the lottery field must be a conscientious journey, balancing the pursuit of technological advancement with the protection of player interests.

The Future of AI in Lottery Predictions: A Prospective Analysis

AS WE CONTEMPLATE THE role of artificial intelligence in predicting lottery outcomes, we are standing at the cusp of a significant technological shift. The journey ahead is filled with both promise and uncertainty. AI, with its immense analytical capabilities and real-time prediction power, could potentially revolutionize the lottery industry. It could also bring about a more secure and fair gaming environment by using deep learning algorithms to detect fraudulent behavior and ensuring the integrity of games.

However, along with the rapid advancement of AI technology comes a new set of challenges. Ensuring the ethical use of large-scale datasets and the privacy of individuals remains a top priority. Striking the right balance between the pursuit of technological innovation and the preservation of ethical standards would be crucial in this evolving landscape.

Moreover, we must bear in mind the inherently unpredictable nature of lotteries. Despite the advances in AI and data analysis, the randomness that defines these games cannot be completely tamed.

Nevertheless, AI can still offer valuable insights and enhance our understanding of patterns in these seemingly random events.

In conclusion, the journey ahead in integrating AI into lottery predictions is a challenging yet exciting one. It is a path that calls for diligent scrutiny, thoughtful deliberation, and unwavering commitment to ethical standards. Only by addressing these challenges head-on can we leverage the full potential of AI, not just to transform the lottery industry, but to also drive forward the larger narrative of responsible technological innovation.

Chapter 17: Free Lottery Prediction Tools for Readers

I n this chapter, we will delve into the fascinating world of free lottery prediction tools available to you readers. These tools represent the democratization of complex mathematical algorithms and AI capabilities, extending far beyond traditional 'quick pick' or 'lucky dip' strategies. They are designed to analyze historical data, identify patterns, and provide predictions, albeit with various levels of accuracy, for forthcoming lottery draws. However, as we explore these tools, it is crucial to remember the underlying principle: no system, regardless of its sophistication, can guarantee a lottery win. The lottery, by design, is a game of probability, and while these tools may influence your choice of numbers, they cannot secure a certain outcome. In the following sections, we will guide you through several of these free tools, discussing their methodologies, strengths, and limitations, and how you, as a reader, can make the most of them.

Lottery Predictor

ONE OF THE POPULAR free lottery prediction tools available is Lottery Predictor. This tool uses an advanced algorithm that takes into account past winning numbers, detecting patterns that the human eye may miss. It offers users a unique perspective, but remember, it doesn't provide a foolproof plan to bag the winning numbers. The tool also comes with an interactive interface that allows you to select your lottery game and input the number of draws for the tool to analyse.

Bear in mind that Lottery Predictor, like all other tools, is subject to the same constraints of randomness and probability inherent in the lottery game. Therefore, while it can potentially improve your odds by identifying patterns in past draws, it cannot guarantee a win. It's essential to use these tools responsibly and as a part of a larger, sensible approach to playing the lottery, taking into account not only mathematical considerations but also your personal budget and attitude to risk.

For more information or to use the Lottery Predictor tool, please visit their website at www.lotterypredictor.com[1].

LottoSmile

ANOTHER TOOL THAT HAS gained popularity among lottery enthusiasts is LottoSmile. This platform claims to help optimize your lottery number selection by providing detailed statistics and probability analysis. It enables users to generate combinations of numbers based on various strategic factors, including hot, cold, and overdue numbers. However, it's crucial to remember that, like all other lottery prediction tools, LottoSmile is not capable of accurately predicting the outcomes. The inherently random nature of the lottery means there is no definitive way to forecast the winning numbers. Using LottoSmile responsibly, within your personal financial and risk boundaries, can add a strategic edge to your approach to the lottery.

For further details or to use the LottoSmile tool, navigate to their website at www.lottosmile.com[2].

---

1.   http://www.lotterypredictor.com

2.   http://www.lottosmile.com

Magayo Lotto

MAGAYO LOTTO IS ANOTHER tool that utilizes sophisticated algorithms to analyze and predict lottery outcomes. It is most notable for its comprehensive approach, considering factors such as the frequency of each number appearing in past draws and the time since each number was last drawn. Yet, the same limitations apply - the tool can suggest trends based on past data, but it cannot override the game's inherent unpredictability. Responsible use of Magayo Lotto, like the other tools discussed, involves keeping in mind your personal budget and risk tolerance.

To learn more about or utilize the Magayo Lotto tool, visit their website at www.magayo.com[3].

Lottery Analyzer

THE LOTTERY ANALYZER offers a unique take on lottery prediction, using AI and machine learning to analyze historical lottery data. This tool parses through data from multiple past draws, identifying potential patterns and trends. However, one must always bear in mind that the randomness of lotteries inherently limits the predictive accuracy of any tool, including the Lottery Analyzer. Therefore, its results should be interpreted with caution, always bearing in mind personal financial capabilities and risk tolerance.

To explore the Lottery Analyzer, visit its website at www.lotteryanalyzer.com[4].

Lottery Predictor

THE LOTTERY PREDICTOR employs a complex algorithm that sifts through extensive data sets of past lottery draws to suggest potential number combinations. Despite its advanced technology, it is

---

3.   http://www.magayo.com

4.   http://www.lotteryanalyzer.com

still subject to the inherent unpredictability of lottery draws. As such, while the Lottery Predictor can offer a more data-driven approach to number selection, it should not be considered a surefire way to secure lottery wins. Its use should always be balanced with an understanding of personal risk boundaries and financial limitations.

To find out more or to use the Lottery Predictor, navigate to their website at www.lotterypredictor.com[5].

AI Lottery

AI LOTTERY TAKES LOTTERY prediction a step further by incorporating neural networks into its analysis. This tool examines lottery data from historical draws, allowing the AI to learn over time and improve its prediction accuracy. However, it is essential to remember that lotteries, by their very nature, are based on chance, limiting the extent to which they can be accurately predicted. Caution should always be exercised when using such tools, with users never betting more than they can afford to lose.

Explore AI Lottery through their website at www.ailottery.com[6].

Predict Lotto

PREDICT LOTTO IS ANOTHER tool that employs AI for predicting lottery outcomes. By analyzing patterns in historical lottery draws, it generates possible number combinations for future draws. Despite its sophisticated technology, the unpredictability of lottery draws means that its predictions are never guaranteed. Therefore, it's critical to use this tool responsibly, keeping personal financial limits in mind.

For more information or to use the Predict Lotto tool, visit their website at www.predictlotto.com[7].

---

5.   http://www.lotterypredictor.com

6.   http://www.ailottery.com

7.   http://www.predictlotto.com

Lotto AI

LOTTO AI IS A STATE-of-the-art tool that leverages machine learning to analyze trends in lottery data, thereby enhancing prediction accuracy. The tool studies past lottery draws, identifying patterns that may be helpful for future predictions. Nonetheless, it's important to remember that the random nature of lotteries inherently constrains the certainty of any prediction. Responsible gambling practices should always be followed when using Lotto AI, meaning that one should only bet what they can afford to lose.

To learn more or to utilize the Lotto AI tool, refer to their website at www.lottoai.com[8].

Neural Lotto

NEURAL LOTTO USES NEURAL network technology to sift through vast amounts of historical lottery data in an attempt to forecast future draw results. It's crucial to understand, however, that while the AI may improve its predictive abilities over time, the inherent randomness of lottery draws precludes any guarantee of success. As always, it is advised to exercise caution when using these tools and never to wager more than one can afford to lose.

To find out more or to employ the Neural Lotto tool, navigate to their site at www.neurallotto.com[9].

Quantum Lotto

QUANTUM LOTTO HARNESSES the power of quantum computing to enhance the predictive ability of lottery outcomes. The tool uses quantum algorithms to process historic lottery data, in attempts to predict future draws. Despite the innovative technology, it's crucial to bear in mind that lotteries are fundamentally random

---

8.   http://www.lottoai.com

9.   http://www.neurallotto.com

events, and therefore, any prediction cannot be fully assured. As with all gambling exercises, responsible practices should be maintained when using Quantum Lotto—meaning, one should only wager what they can comfortably lose.

To discover more or to use the Quantum Lotto tool, visit their website at www.quantumlotto.com[10].

DeepBet

DEEPBET MAKES USE OF deep learning technology to scrutinize extensive lottery data to make educated predictions of future results. While the tool can potentially improve its analytical insights over time, the inherent unpredictability of lottery draws prevents any absolute assurance of success. As ever, it's important to wager responsibly when using such tools, never risking more than is affordable.

To learn more or to employ the DeepBet tool, check their website at www.deepbet.com[11].

AI Lotto Predictor

AI LOTTO PREDICTOR employs artificial intelligence to parse vast amounts of historical lottery data and make informed predictions about future drawings. It's crucial to remember, however, that these estimates, while intelligent, cannot offer guaranteed results due to the inherent randomness of lottery draws. As with all forms of gambling, bet responsibly and only wager what you can afford to lose.

To learn more or to use the AI Lotto Predictor tool, visit their website at www.ailottopredictor.com[12].

---

10.   http://www.quantumlotto.com

11.   http://www.deepbet.com

12.   http://www.ailottopredictor.com

SmartBet

SMARTBET UTILIZES MACHINE learning algorithms to analyze patterns in past lottery data and make predictions about potential results of future draws. Despite the advanced technology and intelligent analysis, it's important to understand that lottery outcomes are fundamentally unpredictable, and thus, the predictions cannot be completely certain. Gamblers should maintain responsible betting habits when using such tools and never risk more than they can comfortably lose.

For further information or to use the SmartBet tool, navigate to their site at www.smartbet.com[13].

QuantPredict

QUANTPREDICT LEVERAGES the power of quantum machine learning to analyze and predict lottery outcomes. This tool, while innovative, is subject to the inherent randomness of lottery draws, and therefore, any prediction cannot be fully assured. As with any form of gambling, it is recommended to bet responsibly and never wager more than you can afford to lose.

To discover more or to use the QuantPredict tool, visit their website at www.quantpredict.com[14].

DataBet

DATABET EMPLOYS SOPHISTICATED data analytics to examine previous lottery results and forecast potential outcomes. While the tool employs intricate algorithms, it is unable to guarantee predictions due to the uncontrolled nature of lottery draws. As with all forms of gambling, players should exercise moderation and wager only what they are financially comfortable with losing.

---

13.   http://www.smartbet.com

14.   http://www.quantpredict.com

For additional details or to use the DataBet tool, access their website at www.databet.com[15].

NeuroLotto

NEUROLOTTO UTILIZES neural networks for its predictive analytics, studying past lottery data to estimate future outcomes. Despite the advanced technology, the inherent randomness of the lottery renders the predictions uncertain. Gamblers should always remember to bet responsibly, not risking more than they can afford to lose.

To learn more or to use the NeuroLotto tool, visit their website at www.neurolotto.com[16].

LotteryLearner

LOTTERYLEARNER INCORPORATES machine learning algorithms to study past lottery data and predict potential results. However, due to the unpredictable nature of lottery draws, the tool can't provide guaranteed predictions. As with all forms of gambling, players are advised to gamble responsibly and within their financial bounds.

For more information or to use the LotteryLearner tool, visit their website at www.lotterylearner.com[17].

PredictoLot

PREDICTOLOT EMPLOYS AI-based predictive analytics to examine previous lottery outcomes and make future forecasts. Despite its technical sophistication, it is important to understand that lottery results are inherently erratic, so guaranteed predictions are not feasible.

---

15. http://www.databet.com

16. http://www.neurolotto.com

17. http://www.lotterylearner.com

Gamblers are urged to play responsibly and not wager beyond their financial comfort zone.

For additional information or to use the PredictoLot tool, access their website at www.predictolot.com[18].

AI-LottoPredict

AI-LOTTOPREDICT APPLIES AI algorithms to analyze historical lottery data and make estimates about upcoming draws. Despite its advanced computational abilities, it is worth noting that the nature of the lottery is essentially unpredictable, making it impossible to provide absolute assurances. Gamblers are always encouraged to wager wisely and within their financial means.

For further details or to utilise the AI-LottoPredict tool, navigate to their website at www.ai-lottopredict.com[19].

NeuroBet

NEUROBET USES NEURAL networks to survey past lottery data and predict possible outcomes. However, given the inherent randomness of lottery events, these predictions should be viewed as estimates, not certainties. Players should always bet responsibly, ensuring they do not gamble more than they can afford to lose.

To find out more or to use the NeuroBet tool, visit their website at www.neurobet.com[20].

LottoAI

LOTTOAI HARNESSES MACHINE learning in its study of previous lottery data, using this information to anticipate future results. Nevertheless, the fickle nature of lottery draws means that these

---

18.   http://www.predictolot.com

19.   http://www.ai-lottopredict.com

20.   http://www.neurobet.com

predictions can't be fully guaranteed. As is the case with all gambling activities, players should only wager what they can comfortably afford to lose.

For more information or to use the LottoAI tool, visit their website at www.lottoai.com[21].

PredictPro

PREDICTPRO UTILIZES deep learning algorithms to scrutinize past lottery data and make predictions for future draws. However, the random and unpredictable nature of lottery draws makes it impossible to guarantee results. Players are always advised to gamble responsibly, ensuring they do not exceed their financial limits.

For additional details or to use the PredictPro tool, visit their website at www.predictpro.com[22].

LotteryMaster

LOTTERYMASTER EMPLOYS sophisticated artificial intelligence techniques to survey past lottery information and project possible outcomes. Given the inherent uncertainty of lottery events, these predictions should be treated as educated guesses rather than absolutes. As always, bettors should gamble responsibly, only risking what they can afford to lose.

To learn more or to use the LotteryMaster tool, navigate to their website at www.lotterymaster.com[23].

JackpotGenius

JACKPOTGENIUS APPLIES cutting-edge machine learning algorithms in its analysis of historical lottery data, using this to forecast

21.   http://www.lottoai.com

22.   http://www.predictpro.com

23.   http://www.lotterymaster.com

future draws. However, due to the inherently random nature of lottery events, it cannot provide absolute guarantees. Players should always wager within their financial means and bet responsibly.

For more information or to use the JackpotGenius tool, visit their website at www.jackpotgenius.com[24].

FutureFortune

EMPLOYING ADVANCED machine learning techniques, FutureFortune analyzes historical lottery data to predict potential outcomes. It is important to note that these predictions are probabilistic due to the inherent randomness of lottery draws. Players should always gamble responsibly. For further details or to use the FutureFortune tool, their website is www.futurefortune.com[25].

WinPredict

WINPREDICT UTILIZES cutting-edge AI technology to examine previous lottery data and estimate future draws. Owing to the random nature of lottery events, these predictions should be regarded as informed estimates rather than definitive outcomes. As always, bet responsibly and within your means. To learn more or to use the WinPredict tool, visit their website at www.winpredict.com[26].

LuckAnalyzer

LUCKANALYZER EMPLOYS sophisticated AI algorithms to sift through past lottery data and predict future outcomes. However, due to the nature of lottery events being inherently random, LuckAnalyzer can only provide calculated estimates. As always gamble responsibly

24.   http://www.jackpotgenius.com

25. http://www.futurefortune.com

26. http://www.winpredict.com

and within your limits. To learn more or to use the LuckAnalyzer tool, visit their website at www.luckanalyzer.com[27].

PrizePredict

PRIZEPREDICT USES MODERN machine learning techniques to analyze historical lottery data and make educated guesses on future draws. These predictions are probabilistic and should be taken as educated guesses rather than absolute outcomes. Always gamble responsibly. For more details or to use the PrizePredict tool, visit their website at www.prizepredict.com[28].

DrawDeducer

DRAWDEDUCER APPLIES advanced AI methods to scrutinize previous lottery data and estimate future results. Given the randomness of lottery draws, these forecasts should be considered as informed estimates. Always bet within your means. To discover more or to use the DrawDeducer tool, navigate to their website at www.drawdeducer.com[29].

LotteryLearner

LOTTERYLEARNER DEPLOYS intricate machine learning algorithms to extrapolate from past lottery data and predict potential outcomes. These predictions are only estimates due to the inherent randomness of lotteries. Remember to always gamble responsibly. For additional information or to use the LotteryLearner tool, visit their website at www.lotterylearner.com[30].

---

27. http://www.luckanalyzer.com

28. http://www.prizepredict.com

29. http://www.drawdeducer.com

30. http://www.lotterylearner.com

FortuneForeseer

FORTUNEFORESEER USES top-notch AI technology to analyze historical lottery data and predict future draws. Due to the random nature of lottery events, these predictions are simply educated estimates. Always bet responsibility and within your means. For further details or to use the FortuneForeseer tool, their website is www.fortuneforeseer.com[31].

JackpotJuggler

JACKPOTJUGGLER EMPLOYS AI algorithms to examine past lottery data and predict future draws. Given the inherently random nature of lottery draws, these predictions are only probabilistic. Always gamble responsibly. To learn more or to use the JackpotJuggler tool, visit their website at www.jackpotjuggler.com[32].

PrizeProphet

PRIZEPROPHET UTILIZES AI to analyze historical lottery data and predict future outcomes. These predictions are probabilistic due to the inherent randomness of lottery draws. Always bet responsibly and within your limits. To discover more or to use the PrizeProphet tool, navigate to their website at www.prizeprophet.com[33].

DrawDynamo

DRAWDYNAMO APPLIES advanced machine learning techniques to analyze historical lottery data and make educated guesses for future draws. These predictions are probabilities, not guarantees, due to the inherently random nature of lottery events. Always gamble responsibly.

---

31. http://www.fortuneforeseer.com

32. http://www.jackpotjuggler.com

33. http://www.prizeprophet.com

For more information or to use the DrawDynamo tool, visit their website at www.drawdynamo.com[34].

LottoLogic

LOTTOLOGIC EMPLOYS AI to sift through past lottery draws and make predictions for future outcomes. However, given the random nature of lottery events, these predictions should be taken as estimates rather than certainties. Always gamble within your means. To learn more or to use the LottoLogic tool, visit their website at www.lottologic.com[35].

FutureFortuna

FUTUREFORTUNA USES sophisticated AI technology to study previous lottery data and anticipate future results. Due to the random nature of lottery events, these predictions are simply informed estimates. Always bet responsibly. To find out more or to use the FutureFortuna tool, their website is www.futurefortuna.com[36].

25 Websites that Offer Free Analytical Tools

1. Data-Driven Documents (D3.js): d3js.org

1. WebDataRocks: webdatarocks.com

1. Excel: office.live.com/start/Excel.aspx

1. Tableau Public: public.tableau.com/en-us/s/gallery

---

34. http://www.drawdynamo.com

35. http://www.lottologic.com

36. http://www.futurefortuna.com

1. Trifacta: trifacta.com

1. RapidMiner: rapidminer.com

1. Talend: talend.com

1. Qlikview: qlik.com/tryqlik

1. Orange: orange.biolab.si

1. H2O: h2o.ai

1. Smartlook: smartlook.com
   Google Analytics: analytics.google.com

1. Clicky: clicky.com

1. Matomo (formerly Piwik): matomo.org

1. Hotjar: hotjar.com

1. Woopra: woopra.com

1. Microsoft Power BI: powerbi.microsoft.com

1. KNIME: knime.com

1. Mixpanel: mixpanel.com

1. Amplitude: amplitude.com

1. SimilarWeb: similarweb.com

1. Pendo: pendo.io

1. Heap: heap.io

1. Crazy Egg: crazyegg.com

1. Open Web Analytics: openwebanalytics.com

Please note: Always check the terms of use for each tool and ensure they meet your specific needs before use.

Conclusion

In our exploration of predicting lottery outcomes with artificial intelligence, we have journeyed through mathematical complexities, technological marvels, and the fascinating world of randomness. We have understood that while the lottery is fundamentally a game of chance, AI tools like LottoLogic and FutureFortuna can provide informed estimates based on past data. Yet, these are estimates, not certainties.

We have also delved into the practical, ethical, and legal implications of using AI in this context, underlining the significance of responsible innovation. The list of 25 websites offering free analytical tools is a testament to the accessibility of data analysis tools in the contemporary landscape, empowering even non-professionals to delve into the world of data.

In closing, it is important to re-emphasize the balance between technological capabilities and human factors involved in the lottery prediction landscape. While AI holds promise, it is not a magic bullet for predicting random events. As we move forward, our understanding of AI's capabilities and limitations in this context will continue to evolve, driving both technological advancements and policy deliberations.

As we have reiterated throughout this book, always gamble within your means and responsibly. The future of AI in lottery prediction is exciting and unknown, a fascinating intersection of probability, technology, and human behavior. This is a journey that is only just beginning, with many more discoveries yet to be made in the quest to predict the unpredictable.

Chapter X: A Step-by-Step Guide to Using AI for Predicting Lottery Numbers

In this chapter, we will explore a detailed step-by-step guide on how to use artificial intelligence in predicting lottery numbers. Remember, this process doesn't guarantee winning but can increase the probability of making more informed choices.

Step 1: Data Collection

Collect historical data of past lottery draws. This data forms the foundation of your AI model. Many lottery organizations publish this information on their websites, or you can use third-party websites that provide such data.

Step 2: Data Preprocessing

Preprocessing involves data cleaning and formatting to make it suitable for building an AI model. Remove any irrelevant information and ensure data uniformity.

Selecting appropriate software is essential to design and implement your AI model effectively. Python, with its comprehensive libraries like Pandas for data preprocessing, NumPy for high-level mathematical functions, and Scikit-learn or TensorFlow for machine learning algorithms, is a popular choice among data scientists. Alternatively, RapidMiner and KNIME are robust data science platforms offering user-friendly interfaces and a wide range of pre-configured AI algorithms. Test several options to find the one that best suits your needs and skill level. Remember, the software is just a tool; understanding the underlying principles of AI and machine learning is crucial for successful model creation and prediction.

Step 3: Identify Patterns

Using machine learning algorithms, identify patterns in the data. For example, you might discover that certain numbers appear together frequently or some numbers have not been drawn in a while.

Visualizing the discovered patterns can provide more intuitive insights into the data. There are several visual representation methods you can explore. For example, using Python's Matplotlib or Seaborn libraries, you can create histograms, bar charts, or heat maps to illustrate the frequency of individual lottery numbers, combinations thereof, or the time since they were last drawn. Another useful visualization is a line plot showing any trends in the frequency of specific number pairs or groups over time. Such visualizations can help you understand the data more comprehensively and support the decision-making process for choosing numbers in future lottery entries.

Step 4: Build the Model

Construct the AI model using the patterns identified. Various algorithms can be applied here, such as regression, decision tree, or neural networks.

Machine learning algorithms are not just formulas, but rather complex procedures that can learn from data. For instance, a regression algorithm might seem like a simple formula, $y = ax + b$, but the process of determining the coefficients 'a' and 'b' involves learning from the dataset. A decision tree algorithm, on the other hand, creates a tree-like model of decisions based on the provided data. It aims to approximate discrete-valued target functions and is one of the simplest yet powerful algorithms.

Neural networks, inspired by the human brain's structure, consist of interconnected layers of nodes or "neurons." They process information using a system of weights and bias adjustments based on the data input. These algorithms are not represented merely as formulas but substantial computational models. Understanding these algorithms requires a deep dive into the principles of machine learning and artificial intelligence. Remember, each algorithm has its strengths and weaknesses, and the choice of algorithm depends on the specific requirements of your project.

Step 5: Training the Model

Train your AI model using your preprocessed data. This step involves the machine learning algorithm learning from the data. It may take several hours or even days, depending on the complexity of the model and the size of the data.

Training the model is a crucial phase in the machine learning process. It refers to the learning that happens when the model is exposed to the dataset. During this phase, the model iteratively makes predictions on the training data and is corrected by making adjustments to its weights and biases. This trial and error process continues until the model's predictions are as accurate as possible, minimizing the difference between the actual output and the predicted output, also known as the error rate.

The training process is governed by a parameter named the learning rate, which determines how fast or slow the model learns. A high learning rate can cause the model to converge too quickly, possibly leading to suboptimal solutions, while a very low learning rate might cause the model to learn too slowly, consuming more time and computational resources. Balancing these factors is critical to efficient model training.

Once the model is thoroughly trained, it should be able to generalize from what it has learned and make accurate predictions on new, unseen data. However, it's important to be wary of overfitting where the model learns the training data too well, capturing noise along with the underlying pattern. Overfitting reduces the model's ability to generalize, leading to poor performance on unseen data. Techniques like cross-validation, regularization, and early stopping are used to prevent overfitting during model training.

In the context of predicting lottery outcomes, the goal of model training would be to identify subtle patterns in historical lottery draw data, learning to predict future draws accurately. However, given the inherently random nature of the lottery, the effectiveness of such a model remains a subject of intense debate and exploration.

Step 6: Testing the Model

Once your model is trained, test its predictions against a separate set of data not used in training. This helps evaluate the model's accuracy. Testing your AI model is a crucial step in the machine learning process. It provides a robust measure of how well your model will generalize to new, unseen data. While the model may perform well on the training data, it's important to ensure it also performs well on data it hasn't encountered before, a concept known as model generalization.

During testing, you'll assess the model's predictions against a separate dataset not used during training, often referred to as the 'test set'. The model's performance here is a good indication of how it will perform in real-world scenarios. Various metrics can be used to evaluate the performance of your model, including accuracy, precision, recall, and F1 score for classification problems; and mean absolute error (MAE), mean squared error (MSE), or root mean squared error (RMSE) for regression problems.

Remember, a model that performs well on the training set but poorly on the test set is likely overfitting the data. Overfitting means that the model has learned the training data too well, including its noise and outliers, and fails to generalize well to new data. Techniques such as cross-validation, regularization, and early stopping are often used to combat overfitting.

Testing the model is not a one-time process. As new data becomes available and as the model is put to use, you'll want to continuously test and refine it to ensure it remains accurate and relevant.

Step 7: Predicting the Numbers

After training and testing, use the model to predict future lottery numbers. Be aware that these are still probabilities, not certainties.

Predicting lottery numbers with an AI model is a complex task, primarily due to the inherent randomness of lottery draws. Nonetheless, the model will sift through historical lottery data, seeking patterns or trends that may not be immediately apparent. It uses these insights to calculate probabilities for future lottery numbers. However, it's crucial to understand that despite its sophisticated analytical capabilities, the AI cannot provide a guaranteed prediction. The output is probabilistic, meaning it identifies numbers that, based on previous patterns, have a higher likelihood of being drawn. But, like any probabilistic prediction, there is always a chance of inaccuracy. It's a game of odds and probabilities, and even AI can't change that fundamental aspect of lotteries. Moreover, the ethical and legal implications of using AI in this manner should be carefully considered to ensure responsible innovation.

Step 8: Refining the Model

Over time, continue refining your AI model with new data. As more lottery numbers are drawn, add this data to your model to improve its predictive capability.

Remember, while AI can help identify patterns and improve the odds, it cannot guarantee a lottery win. It's always essential to gamble responsibly.

Step 9: Advanced Refinement Techniques

Delving deeper into refining the model, we must not overlook advanced techniques that could potentially increase the model's accuracy. This involves additional layers of complexity and computational processing but can yield significant improvements. Techniques like **deep learning,** which allows the model to self-learn through experience, or **ensemble methods,** which combine various machine learning models to achieve better predictive performance, could be considered. It might also be useful to implement **feature engineering,** a process designed to create new features or modify existing ones to better capture the underlying data patterns. Despite these advanced methods, remember that each additional adjustment adds complexity and may require more computational power, time, and expertise. However, these refinements could potentially lead to an enhanced probability of predicting lottery numbers, always keeping in mind the inherent randomness involved in the process.

.

Also by Gary Covella, Ph.D.

Money for Nothing: Unlocking the Secrets of Grants, Scholarships, and Other Free Benefits

Think Rich Live Rich: How to Build a Profitable Online Business and Live the Life of Your Dreams

Co-Hosting on Airbnb: The Ultimate Guide to Making Money Without Owning Real Estate

The Ultimate Guide to Remote and Digital Side Hustles: Thriving in a Post-Pandemic World

Course Development Cashflow: Monetize Your Knowledge Through Content Course Creation

Entrepreneur's Handbook: Establishing a Successful Money Broker Business

Laptop Millionaire: Unleashing Your Wealth Potential and Building a Laptop-Based Empire

Monetizing Product Review: Strategies for Profit and Free Product Opportunities

Online Resources for Job Seekers: Tools and Platforms for Success

The AI Entrepreneur: How Artificial Intelligence Can Make You Wealthy

Virtual Call Centers Made Easy: Start Your Own Virtual Call Center Business Today

Effortless Weight Loss: Burning Fat and Dropping Pounds Starting Today

AI Tutor : Harnessing ChatGPT for Revolutionary Education Programs

AI-Enhanced Cryptocurrencies: A Revolutionary Approach to Blockchain Development

The Millionaire Mindset: How to Get Rich With the Power of Your Mind

Global Startup Success: How to Build a Profitable International Business from Home on a Shoestring Budget

Flying Free: The Ultimate Guide to Earning Your Private Pilot License After 50

AI and the Lottery: Defying Odds with Intelligent Prediction

About the Author

Gary Covella, Ph.D., is an esteemed author and authority in the business field, known for enriching the industry with multiple seminal books that blend scholarly insight with practical expertise. His comprehensive work, driven by a profound academic background, continues to guide professionals and organizations towards strategic growth and innovative business practices.

Milton Keynes UK
Ingram Content Group UK Ltd.
UKHW040709201123
432908UK00001B/229